THE

WORLD

OF

BEES

by Murray Hoyt

BONANZA BOOKS • NEW YORK

Library of Congress Catalog Card Number: 65–13277
Manufactured in the United States of America

Chapter 14 appeared in slightly different form under the title "How to Get Along With the Bees" in the June 16, 1962, issue of *The Saturday Evening Post* (Curtis Publishing Company).

This edition published by Bonanza Books,
a division of Crown Publishers, Inc.,
by arrangement with the author
a b c d e f g h

THIS BOOK IS DEDICATED

to the Malcolm Randall family in the special hope that Steve and Chris and Greg and Jeff and Leslie Marie may someday, with its help, come to admire and like the world of bees as much as does their grandfather.

ACKNOWLEDGMENTS

I would like to thank all the people who have helped me in the preparation of this book. To mention each separately, with thanks commensurate with his contribution, would make another small book. Obviously the publishers would never stand still for this. So I shall limit my list to a very few.

My special thanks, then, to Charles Mraz, of Middlebury, Vermont, for unstinting cooperation on text and picture-taking. And to his bees for allowing themselves to be disrupted in their daily toil for model work.

And to Ben Rogers, of the Rogers Photo Service, in Middlebury, who photographed these tiny models.

To Roger A. Morse, entomologist, of Cornell University, for making his latest experiments available to me.

To Carl Johnson for the pictures he sent.

To Ellis Amburn of Coward McCann for sympathizing editorially with my problems.

To Margaret, my wife, just for being with me during composition, and for overlooking preoccupation.

To these and all others, my heartfelt thanks.

MURRAY HOYT

CONTENTS

Illustrations will be found following page 96

I

---◆·◆---

STINGING INSECTS

To the average person, a bee is any insect he thinks might be able to sit down on him with results painful to him.

Wasps, hornets, even some buzzing flies come under this heading as far as he's concerned, and he wants no part of any of them, especially of their extreme southern exposures when they are headed north. This whole attitude is perfectly exemplified by a large, shorts-clad vacationist I once saw whacking hysterically with a road map at a male wasp (which couldn't possibly sting because he has no equipment to sting with) and screaming, "A bee! He'll bite me!" Why such people use the word "bite" instead of "sting" when they know it's done with the other end, is one of apiculture's mysteries.

This is the bee image held by a very large percentage of the citizenry. It would be hard to make up an image, even if you tried, which would be more diametrically opposite the true facts; an oversimplified, erroneous concept of a highly complex little creature and his very sophisticated world.

It is therefore the wistful, possibly naïve, purpose of this book to change that image with as many people as possible.

The world of bees is actually a completely fascinating world, and in some of its facets almost incredible. Certainly in this category is the proven fact that a queen bee is fertilized by the male bee at *only one period of her life*. And from that fertilization she lays eggs that are fertile for the rest of her life. If it were a short life, or if she laid only a few eggs, it wouldn't be astonishing, perhaps. But a good queen will lay up to *3,000* eggs a day depending on the needs of the hive. And she may lay eggs, though not that many, for up to four or five *years*. An inconceivable number of fertile eggs from just the *one* mating period.

And even bee experts refused, when the communication theory was first advanced in Germany and before it had been proved, to believe that the tiny brain of a honeybee over the centuries had perfected a complex system of intercommunication through "dancing" on the combs after the discovery of a fine source of food, which told other workers precisely which direction to fly and how far to go to find that food.

Even this they might have been willing to believe if the theory hadn't further stated that the dance was done at an angle from the perpendicular which represented the angle from the sun at which the other worker bees were to fly.

This presupposed an ability on the part of a bee to figure angles which would do credit to a geometry major. After she'd figured and remembered them, she then had to fly them perfectly after leaving the hive.

Oh come now! A little insect not much more than half an inch long? Impossible! But if you think those examples are fascinating or incredible, how much more incredible is this one. Worker bees, who themselves are undeveloped females, upon occasion, pick an egg—any egg—laid by their queen bee in a standard wax cell. This egg would, in the normal course of events, produce an undeveloped female like themselves.

But they tear out and enlarge the cell around that egg, and feed the resulting larva with a special food. Presto, they have a queen bee with fully developed female organs, capable of doing all the egg laying for their hive. When their queen is accidentally killed they produce a queen in this way.

Change the sex of an egg already laid? Completely against all the rules of nature.

Well, nobody's been able to convince the bees that they can't do it. They do it every now and then, and it's just one more of the amazing impossibilities of their wonderful world.

Bees are hymenopterous insects. So are ants, wasps, hornets, solitary bees, ichneumon flies, sawflies and many others. The name comes from two Greek words meaning "membrane" and "wing." Thus they are membrane-winged insects, and are considered to be the highest group of invertebrates in structure and instincts. Many of them live in colonies; among those that do are hornets, bumblebees, ants. And of course honeybees.

I believe that honeybees have advanced communal living further than any other creature that exists on our globe. The ant-lovers will probably give me an argument and that is their right. Certainly the Communist countries, Russia, Red China et al., aren't even in the same league. The bees do it the way a Khrushchev or a Mao would hope that someday they could, come the millennium. Maybe the reason the Communists can't do it as well as the bees is because all their workers aren't undeveloped females.

Some of the other hymenoptera are built a little like bees, and to the uninitiated, look a little like them. And thus bees get blamed for their stings. Yellow jackets are, I think, most often mistaken for honeybees. They're smaller, and a little yellower even than a good strain of Italian bee. Yellow jackets have very short tempers.

The bumblebee is a very large bee and it is hard to see how it could be mistaken for a honeybee, but often it is. Wasps, on the other hand, are longer and thinner than a honeybee. They give the impression of being in two parts attached to each other by a thread. Obviously it's more than a thread or the front end wouldn't be able to wield the stinger in the other end with such muscular and venomous abandon. But it looks like a thread. From this threadlike middle comes the term "wasp-waisted" which the trussed-up and corseted women of another era tried so desperately to emulate.

Perhaps the surest (but the most painful) method of telling the difference between other stingers and honeybees is to be stung. If there's no stinger or poison sac in the stung place after you brush the insect off, and if it moves to another place and instantly stings again, that's not a honeybee. The others can sting as often as they want to—and believe me they want to—but a honeybee can sting only once, because her stinger has tiny barbs on it which hold in your flesh once they're in there. The stinger, together with the bee's whole poison sac, is torn from her body, leaving a gaping hole at the end. She crawls around a bit, and must suffer considerably. And she dies. There might remain the will to sting a second time and the life to do it. But the weapon is gone.

The males of some of these stinging insects have no stinger. They, too, might work up the desire now and then, but they just haven't the equipment. In the winged-insect world, males don't amount to much. Nature must have felt that giving anything that unimportant a method of defense was wasteful.

Drone (male) honeybees fall into this category; also male bumblebees and male wasps. The drone honeybee is bigger than a worker, shorter than a queen. He's not hard to identify. The male wasp has a white or yellow face, while the female's face is black.

That woman vacationist whom I mentioned earlier as slapping at the male wasp, thought she was witnessing black magic when I calmed her, caught the wasp in my hand and held it gently while she and her husband drove away with the air of people who wanted no part of witchcraft or its perpetrator. I've many times picked up a wasp in each hand when their buzzing in a window was disrupting and frightening a whole area of a public dining room. I make absolutely sure the wasps have a white or yellow face, but the onlookers don't know I'm making sure. It's pleasant to see *their* faces, hear the awed and frightened ohs and ahs. I know then how a good magician feels when his trick comes off well.

So even in cases where you come upon insects and might be stung by them, if the species and sex is right, there is absolutely no danger. There are many variations of all these insects in many countries.

Especially it is true that with honeybees you have little to fear. It seems almost as if honeybees know that to sting would kill them. They do just what you would do yourself under similar circumstances; they suffer a lot before they'll commit suicide to punish you. I've seen a beekeeper, moving quietly in broad daylight and stripped to the waist, take apart one of his hives that contained roughly 50,000 bees. He did what he had to do, put the hive back together again, all without a single sting. Maybe they remembered that he had done this many times before and always had left the bees none the worse for it. They weren't about to die when it would accomplish nothing.

Perhaps I'm attributing to bees a power to reason which they do not have. But personally, having watched some of their incredible accomplishments in other areas, I'm fairly sure they *do* possess a very primitive power to reason.

So the one factor which, more than any other, distorts the image of the honeybee, her ability to sting, is magnified by ignorance and fear to an unbelievable degree. The distortion is further fed and increased by mistaken identity and the vicious stings of other insects, all of them lumped together and blamed on honeybees. Don't misunderstand me. The sting of a honeybee is a very real and very painful thing. If you have an allergy to bee venom, one sting could, to give it its worst interpretation, kill you. We'll examine this matter of bee venom allergy in detail in a later chapter and show you how, even should you suffer such an allergy, you can make yourself completely safe.

Granted, as I say, that a honeybee can sting and does upon occasion. The occasions are rare, and very rare indeed in relation to the number of stings blamed on honeybees. Your share of stings can be further cut by knowledge of bee habits and customs, information which I shall give you as we go along.

Meanwhile, and partly because of the bad image, the economic impact of honeybees on the countries of the world, which runs into many billions of dollars, is ignored or not understood, or both. Do I see raised eyebrows over that figure of billions of dollars in benefits to humanity? Let's examine those benefits.

The value of the honey crop in the United States alone in 1963 was $53,929,000. This was for a total of 299,000,000 pounds. Somebody with a big shiny new computer ought to figure out how many laborious honeybee flights from hive to flowers and return would be represented by that many pounds. In addition to the honey, 5,460,000 pounds of beeswax were produced and it was worth $2,420,000 to the producers.

This honey crop was 10 percent above the '62 crop, and 9 percent above the '61 crop, which was the previous record. There were 5,536,000 colonies held in United States apiaries that year and these averaged 54 pounds each of surplus honey taken off. North Dakota led the nation in that category with a whopping average of 128 pounds per colony. South Dakota worked its bees almost as hard, averaging 3 pounds less per colony.

Huge as these sums may seem to all but government legislators, they are only a drop in the bucket compared to the figures for world production. No one actually knows these figures, because no survey is made in most of the backward countries of the world.

In turn, even the world figures would be only a drop in the bucket compared to the indirect benefits bestowed upon agriculture by the bees through the pollination of crops.

Pasture lands, crop areas, fruit trees, in short almost all plants and trees, must be pollinated. If this were not done there would not be enough food for the largest percentage of the people living in the world today.

There would be no bread in the stores, no cereals, almost none of the products we eat today which come from the farm. Any effort on our part to substitute meat for fruits or vegetables or cereals would be defeated because there would be nothing for meat animals to live on, either. Our whole food structure is based on pollination.

Pollination can be carried out in several ways. The plant may self-pollinize, that is, pollen may drop from one part of that plant onto another part; wind may carry the pollen from one plant to another; and insects may carry the pollen.

Plants which depend on their own pollen for long periods exclusively have been proved by rather extensive experiments gradually to deteriorate. They need a shot of outside blood.

The wind is a fickle instrument and sometimes may not blow. If it does, it may blow from the wrong direction. The nearest plant similar to the one which needs pollination may be too far away for pollen on the wind to reach. Or the plant may be shielded. For those plants which cannot mature their seeds by self-pollination, and there are many of them, insects are absolutely essential.

Insect pollination is accomplished by four groups of insects. The first group consists of the lower forms of insects like beetles, butterflies, moths and flies. The second group is made up of the solitary bees. The third is made up of the bumblebees, and the fourth is made up of the honeybees.

Lower insects visit flowers only when they themselves are hungry. Some of them haven't the tiny hairs to carry pollen efficiently, notably the beetles. Once their hunger of the moment is appeased, their carrying of pollen stops. We'd all of us be in a bad way if we depended entirely upon them.

The solitary bees are almost as bad. They do feed their young, but they don't store food, and they don't visit flowers except on a need-of-the-moment basis.

Bumblebees have brood nests, feed their young, and store some honey. But they're too big to visit parts of our floral life to their advantage and ours; and there aren't many of them.

Honeybees, then, do the bulk of the pollinating. They work among the flowers every good day, all day, from morning till night, as fast as they can work. The more blossoms that need their attention, the harder they work; it has nothing to do with hunger-of-the-moment. They're storing for winter. They even begin to increase their brood nests (their eggs, larva, pupa and hatching bees) in the spring, ahead of the time when their area will be full of blossoms. They want as many of their own hive representatives as possible to be visiting when those blossoms do appear.

The first three types of pollinators are not controlled by man. But the honeybees can be controlled and are.

The beekeeper uses every ingenious device he can think of to stimulate his colonies to increase brood nests ahead of the honeyflow. This is, after all, only an attempt to make easy for the bees and their queen something which is instinctive with them anyway. He makes sure there are enough empty cells in the right place in the hive to be visited for egg laying by the queen. He sees that their stored pollen supply is adequate for feeding the brood. He makes sure there is enough honey for feeding the young. He makes sure the hive is strong. He replaces the queen if she gives any signs of being too old to do a satisfactory job of egg laying.

But this still would not represent enough control to handle the needs of, for instance, the vast orchards of the Shenandoah Valley, the vineyards and cotton fields of the San Joaquin Valley, the vast alfalfa and clover fields of dairyland. In these and other areas of vast concentration of crops, sometimes covering miles and miles of countryside, bees of the neighborhood, under ordinary conditions, would be completely unable to handle the situation. They'd be overwhelmed by the magnitude of their good fortune. They would naturally fly only as far into this mass of bloom as they needed to, to fill their honey stomachs. There would be plenty of blossoms within a matter of a few hundred yards for this purpose, and the center of the field or orchard, miles away, would be virtually unvisited.

So the orchardman and the farmer get together with the

beekeeper and control matters even further. Sometimes they pay the beekeeper a set fee per colony to place his colonies in yards throughout the area of their bloom. If there are a lot of beekeepers competing for this chance to make many pounds of extra honey, the beekeeper may distribute his hives throughout the orchard or field free.

Occasionally the orchardman or farmer sees a chance personally to control matters, and to make a profit at the same time. He himself becomes the beekeeper, spacing his colonies carefully in yards throughout his holdings. If he expects a particularly fine crop of blossom and doesn't own or can't rent the bees he feels are necessary to pollinate it, he will buy enough five-pound packages of bees-with-queen from men whose business is raising and selling such packages, to handle the situation. These will be timed to arrive by mail three or four days before the blossoms start to come out, to give the bees time to acclimate themselves to the area.

If he hasn't enough hives to accommodate the packages he is buying, he may even establish them in some sort of wooden or metal makeshift box or barrel for a hive. He may destroy them after the honeyflow is over to get what honey they did store, but they will have accomplished what he was interested in having them accomplish. They will have visited his blossoms and increased his crops.

How much will such control increase his crops? The United States Department of Agriculture and many universities have conducted experiments over the years designed to answer this question.

The testers devised all sorts of ingenious ways to get the facts they wanted. They screened small test areas to keep bees and other pollinating insects out. They screened other areas to keep bees in. They staked out an area and counted every insect that visited it, writing down the number of visitors of each kind in a given number of hours to visit that one area. They devised many other tests in orchards, alsike clover fields, and in other crop areas. A scientist who wants to get at the true facts, and has the time and money, can think of some extremely ingenious tests.

Bees proved to be the overwhelming winners in these pollination tests in every case. The scientists proved, for instance, that better than 82 percent of the insects visiting a staked-out area were honeybees. One insect survey done by Cornell University and involving 459 man-hours, could establish only 7.75 insects per man-hour, other than honeybees, visiting the test area in an orchard. Obviously those less than eight insects seen per hour would have done a poor job for the orchardist without honeybee help.

In one orchard where there had been a crop failure one year, an insect survey showed that there would not be enough other insects *and* bees, lumped together, properly to pollinate again the next season. Another failure was indicated. So the scientists got the owner to hire twenty two-story beehives for that orchard. And he harvested a wonderful crop.

In inclement weather, honeybees were found to be even more a necessity in orchard or grove work. If rain or any other mood of nature cuts drastically the time during the blossom cycle that insects can visit flowers, the effectiveness of uncontrolled insects is cut even below its usual low level. Only a huge force of bees can get the job done in the time available. There are roughly 1,000,000 blossoms on an acre of adult apple trees. But given only a few hours of acceptable weather, the force of about a million bees represented by twenty colonies in an orchard can make a lot of calls per bee and thus care for quite a few acres.

Too, the grains of pollen are so small that a single bee

can carry on its hairy body many thousands of them. And a 5 percent orchard "set" is all that is necessary to produce a reasonable crop. Plenty of honeybees in position and ready at the end of bad weather, then, can take advantage of every second of good weather to help the fruit grower. But in unhappy stretches of weather, wild insects are even less effective than under normal circumstances.

But of course everyone has known and admitted for generations that honeybees are important in orchard work. Let's look at a representative field crop like alsike clover seed growing where a five percent seed set, acceptable to orchardists, would spell ruin for the farmer. His effort is to come as near 100 percent as is humanly (and beely) possible. Every one percent added to the set is money jingling in the operator's pocket.

All tests proved that the value of the seed produced by self-pollination was so low that it would nowhere near cover even the cost of harvesting the crop. Wind-pollinated plants set 3.4 seeds per head.

But pollinizing with a three-frame nucleus of honeybees gave an average of over 120 seeds per head. Thus alsike clover, properly cross-pollinated by bees, will yield about 15 bushels of seed per acre. With bees excluded, the most that would be raised would be about six-tenths of one bushel per acre.

Even in the case of red clover, a legume that honeybees were supposed to leave strictly to the bumblebees because the honeybee tongue was thought to be too short to tap the nectar, similar experiments showed that 82 percent of the pollination visits were made by honeybees, 15 per cent by bumblebees and 3 percent by other insects.

Each crop differs from every other. But always honeybees do the bulk of the work. They insure good yields where they are present in numbers. Conversely, where the farmer or orchardist has made no attempt to see that his bees (or someone else's) are ready at blossom time, a poor crop results. And all this makes a dramatic difference in the amount of money coming in.

Visualize, then, the vast orchards of the world, the thousands upon thousands of miles of clover and alfalfa, the vast groves of the citrus belt extending around the world, the berry fields, the yellow-blanket trefoil fields, the vast and awesome acreage of other segments of the globe's agricultural complex that need insect pollination.

Think, too, upon the dramatic difference in yield between a bee-pollinated area carefully controlled, and one pollinated in some other way; the more than fifteen extra bushels of alsike clover seed per acre, the 82 percent visitation of honeybees to red clover, the section of orchard that failed one year and showed potential failure the next until honeybees were rushed in. Think of the vast monetary difference these surveys and incidents represent.

Then put the two images together in your mind. Suddenly the "billions of dollars" of benefits to humanity takes on meaning, becomes real. You think upon these things, and it is a conservative and reasonable fact of our lives. There is no way that man can know completely his dependence on bees. But he can know that it is tremendous. The picture of it takes shape in his mind vaguely, mistily. Yet it is clear enough so that its vastness is dramatically apparent.

And all this has been going on for untold centuries. There is little doubt but that bees were around long, long before man. Fossils earlier than man show us flora which are now bee-pollinated; there is no reason to believe that they weren't bee-pollinated then. Fossilized bees have been found in geological strata which predate man by millions of years. Amber

of ungaugeable antiquity has contained bee fossils. Their
body structure then was very much as it is today.

Cave men left pictures of bees on their cave walls, some of
which are thought to be fifteen thousand years old. One in
the Paleolithic Era found on a rock in a cave in Valencia,
Spain, shows two men climbing ropes to rob a bee colony,
taking the honeycomb and placing it in baskets. In Egypt
the carvings on objects of antiquity, including tombs, show
the honeybee. The mummies of that land were embalmed
with an unknown fluid, and some authorities say that it was
based on honey. Most astonishing of all, jars have been found
containing embalmed infants, the rest of the space in the
jar filled with honey. It is no longer particularly astonishing that the ancient dead should have been preserved. But
that this should have been done in honey is amazing. Even
more amazing is the fact that tests showed the honey itself
to be in fine condition, too.

The Bible says, "A land flowing with milk and honey."
Obviously somebody had to practice a crude apiculture to
get the honey. Jesus, after He had returned from the dead,
said, according to Luke in Chapter 24, verses 41–42, "Have
ye here any meat?" The quotation continues, "And they
gave him a piece of a broiled fish and of an honeycomb."
King Solomon says in Proverbs 24, verse 13, "My son, eat
thou honey, because it is good." Proverbs 16, verse 24 says,
"Pleasant words are as an honeycomb, sweet to the soul, and
health to the bones."

In Bible times comb honey was not produced in neat
pound boxes with sheets of starter drawn out and filled by the
bees as it is today. The bees stored it in irregular combs which
they made to fit the space available. The colony was in most
cases destroyed to get this comb and its honey store. And the
comb was cut or broken into chunks and given people to

eat. Honey seems, judging from ancient writings, to have been most important in countries which did not raise much sugarcane.

Greek and Roman literature abounds with references to honey and bees. When Pompey and 1,000 men were marching through the mountains, their enemies placed crocks of poisoned honey along the route. Pompey's men ate it, became unconscious, and were immediately attacked and killed.

Aristotle wrote about bees and honey with almost unbelievable insight and accuracy. He also engaged in a bit of exaggeration, calling it "dew distilled from the stars and the rainbow."

Either more was known about honeybees in those ancient times than we realize, or Aristotle himself was far in advance of everyone else in his knowledge. In his day kings were all-powerful. He therefore made the mistake of calling the queen a "king bee." And he thought there was more than one "ruler in the hive." He did not understand the production of wax, and believed it was gathered from the flowers and carried to the hive, like pollen, on the legs of the bees. Since in those days there were no glass hives, and any observations of hive life were full of peril, it is small wonder that he made a few errors.

In one area particularly, Aristotle departed radically from the beliefs of his time. He decided that the "rulers" had much to do with reproduction, and he described the development of the bee beginning with the larva stage, almost as we know it to be today. The theory with which this clashed was one of the most astonishing of all science. Bees were thought by most people to develop from the body of a dead ox.

"Kill an ox and confine it in a one-room building, closing with clay every opening. Then open the building on the 32nd day, and you will find it full of bees, crowded in clusters on each other, and the horns and the bones and the hair and nothing else of the bullock left." Probably the ancient was like the average man today; he mistook buzzing flies for bees.

You can understand that a man had to have the courage of his convictions to come out in opposition to such a dramatic idea as this. It seems absurd to us today, but it was embraced for generations.

Honey itself was supposed to have been the food of the gods of most early civilizations. Obviously, if the people considered a particular food a rare treat, it was only natural that in their mythology their gods would eat quantities of it. The people thought of the food they would choose if they were gods, and assumed their gods chose it. Thus the Greek gods on Mount Olympus ate quantities of honey. And the Viking gods of the Norsemen gained strength from it.

All through recorded time honey has been noted as a source of quick energy. It is absorbed into the bloodstream faster than any other sweet. It does not go through a process of digestion as we know it, because the bees in their honey stomachs have done much of this for us. It is said to be predigested. But, to quote Irvin Cobb: "They fail to state by whom."

Athletes in the early Olympic games were fed honey just before competing. Mead, made by mixing honey and water, was an energy drink of the Britons and the Germanic tribes. Experiments have been conducted lately which have proved that in the feeding of infants and oldsters whose digestive processes have been impaired, honey is assimilated without digestive upsets and does not cause diarrhea.

Dr. Jarvis a few years ago, in a book called *Folk Medicine* which was on the best seller lists for over a hundred weeks, advocated the use of a mixture of honey and vinegar for many ills. The American Medical Association (of which, incidentally, Dr. Jarvis is a member) was unenchanted with the book. But enough people were helped, or thought they were, to spread the word to others and gain it a sale seldom accorded any book except the Bible itself. Dr. Jarvis's book was given its greatest sales impetus when a columnist tried the Jarvis remedy for sinus difficulties (the chewing of comb honey or just honey cappings) with spectacular results, which he described in his nationally syndicated column.

Honey is an antiseptic, and was used, mixed with milk, by the high-born ladies of Roman history as a skin beauty aid. Chinese beauties used a mixture of almond oil and honey in the same way.

In 1934 Professor Mykola H. Haydak, of the University of Minnesota, undertook to explore the possibilities of the Biblical "land flowing with milk and honey." Was this the perfect diet combination as the Bible seemed to imply? It *sounded* delightful, but he could find no record of anyone who had actually tried it. He therefore started such a diet on the eve of Thanksgiving Day. Three tablespoons of honey were dissolved in a little milk, and then mixed with the rest of a quart of milk. He drank one pint of this mixture every two hours from eight in the morning till eight at night.

He continued the experiment for twelve weeks—almost a quarter of a year. The first week he was very hungry, but this phase then passed. His weight remained constant throughout the twelve weeks. He even felt more vigorous than usual. There was no constipation or any other difficulty of elimination.

However, he had realized when he started that the diet would be lacking in vitamin C. In the second month his skin became dry, pimples marred his face, and whitish round spots appeared on his tongue. He added ten ounces of orange

juice a day, and all these symptoms disappeared for the dura-
tion of the experiment. So perhaps the "land flowing with
milk and honey" should be changed to "a land flowing with
milk and honey and ten ounces of orange juice."

We find, then, that bees aren't the villains they are considered to be throughout the land. On the contrary, we owe
much of our food and our riches to them. Possibly we owe
them even our lives.

From the earliest recordings of antiquity our friends the
bees have been unobtrusively blessing the lives of all of us.

2

---◆◆---

BEE ANATOMY AND SEX

If in each political entity of the world most of the members were without any sex; and if the president or mayor were a woman—the only female among us and the one who did all the reproducing—it would be a fantastic setup. Our lives would be completely different—work-filled. And most of us would feel ours was an uninteresting life in the extreme.

Yet that is the basic situation in a nation of honey bees. The queen bee is the one female in the hive. The workers, the bees we see gathering nectar in the fields, are undeveloped females, or neuters. Except for the queen they comprise 100 percent of the hive's population in winter, and nearly that in spring and summer. In those seasons there are also the true males, called drones.

These are tolerated by the workers for a while because new young queens are to hatch and there must be drones for their mating. But in the winter, when every ounce of food is tremendously important and there are no queens hatching, the males are forced outside to freeze or starve to death. I hope the women of our world who read this don't get ideas.

The queen is longer than the worker or the drone, the

drone is next in size, and the worker is the smallest of the three.

If you compare their structure with that of a human, the first and most noticeable difference is that the skeleton of the bee is on the outside, and protects the soft parts of the body. The skeleton of a human is inside, covered by the soft parts. If the bee skeleton were in one piece it would be no more flexible than a turtle shell. The bee couldn't bend. Instead it is made up in sectors held together by flexible hinges.

A honeybee is divided into three parts. The head has the mouth parts, the eyes and the antennae. The thorax, which is the middle part of the bee, anchors three legs and two wings on each side, and holds the muscles to control these. The abdomen contains the honey stomach, the regular stomach, the stomach mouth, and a large sac which forms the end of the ailmentary canal. At the tip of the abdomen are the poison sac and the stinger. On the back, down almost to the stinger, is the opening of a scent gland. On the underside are the wax glands and the pores through which the wax comes out and accumulates in flakes under the fourth to seventh segments of the bee's abdominal skeleton. The three sections of the bee are separated from each other by two pinched-in areas. These are not, however, as pinched in or as threadlike as the waist of a wasp.

Some of these parts interest humans especially, because they have to do with the particular functions of the bee in our lives.

To begin with, bees go us three better in the matter of eyes; they have five of them. Two are large and compound, and there are also three simple eyes at the top of the face. Von Frisch has proved that the eyes of the bee polarize the light rays like a prism.

The jaws of the bee are hung like ours, but move sideways instead of up and down.

The antennae, or feelers, are very sensitive to the touch and contain, of all things, the organs of smell. They also probably contain the organs of hearing. Without antennae it would be very difficult for the field bee to stick to one type of flower—and one only—on a particular flight. And if this were not possible it would complicate the correct pollination of our food plants and trees.

The bee's tongue, according to Snodgrass, who is called the world's greatest authority on the anatomy of the honeybee, has at its tip a delicate lobe which is spoonlike, and is known as the labellum. This tongue has a tiny groove running the length of it on the underside and continuing as a tube into the spoon at the end. Even the minutest amount of nectar will move up this track by capillary attraction. But if there's a whole lot of nectar, the bee just sucks it up much as we form our tongue and lips into a sucking mechanism. The forehead of the worker contains the glands which produce a whitish liquid brood food called "royal jelly," on which the continuance of the colony depends.

The legs of the bee, all six of them, are also geared for food collection. The food is pollen, which is a bee's protein and is used especially in the feeding of the brood. Brood cannot be raised successfully without it.

Pollen is in dustlike grains called microspores. These grains vary in size from one one-hundredth of an inch to one three-thousandth of an inch. That's fairly small. The bee collects pollen by a sort of five-ringed circus which would put a television juggler to shame. The five rings are the mouth parts, the coat of tiny featherlike hairs on its body, and the three sets of legs. At times everything is moving at once with not much apparent relation to anything else.

The mouth parts bite and scrape the pollen from the anthers of flowers, which are the pollen-producing parts. Pollen is scraped up by the tongue, and collected on the coat of hairs and even on the antennae. The mouth moistens it with nectar; in fact wets it enough so that dry pollen that never reaches the mouth gets moistened too.

There is a set of antenna cleaners on each of the two front legs. These comb the pollen off the antennae and transfer the pollen to the mouth. Then there are stiff, comblike hairs on the back legs, which comb the pollen off the body. All the pollen gradually ends up as two tiny loaves of bread— but immense in comparison with the size of the bee itself— in the pollen basket on each hind leg, held in the hollow of the leg and by the fringe of hairs.

You'll notice we haven't mentioned the middle legs, but they are functional and part of this vaudeville performance, too. They take the pollen from the mouth, and transfer it to the pollen baskets and pack it there so that it will stay.

Mind you, all these things are going on at once. Things are being combed and transferred, and chewed, and moistened, and packed almost like sleight of hand. Each set of legs is moving independently of the others. Add the fact that the performance can take place while the bee is doing something else, even flying to the next flower, and so rapidly that the eye can't follow more than a fraction of one part of it during each observation, and it becomes even more fantastic. You must actually see it to appreciate the sum total of the activity.

When the bee gets back to the hive she finds a suitable cell, hangs her loaded hind legs over it, and holds on with her forelegs. Then, with the middle legs, she pushes the pollen loaves from the baskets into the cell.

As if this weren't enough, the legs have one further function. On their ends are claws with which the bee clings to rough surfaces. But when she walks up the side of a smooth painted post, or up the face of a glass window, or even upside down on glass, there is nothing for those claws to hold onto.

There is, however, a pad of flesh and tiny hairs at the base of the claws. And the act of the claws in straining for a hold forces out onto this pad a tremendously efficient and sticky glue. The pad comes against the surface, the glue holds, and the bee walks around on anything at all, no matter how smooth.

The wings, too, are attached to the thorax, two on each side, hooked to each other by infinitesimal hooks so that they are converted into one wing and work together. They are not worked up and down by muscles attached directly to them. The muscles are attached to the back plates of the thorax, and elevate and drop those back plates, which in turn move the wings and allow the bees to go to the field, get us the honey, and return to the hive loaded with it.

The honey sac, or honey stomach, of the bee is her collection and carrying tank. The collected nectar is taken into this honey stomach, and later transferred to another bee or bees in the hive so that they can store it. Sticking up into the honey stomach from the digestion stomach below, is a cone with an X-shaped valve in it. It is called the stomach mouth. The valve lets into the regular stomach any amount of nectar or honey which the bee requires for food for herself.

The main difference between the workers and the queen, aside from size, lies in the reproductive organs of the queen. This is the egg-laying mechanism which produces and fertilizes up to 3,000 eggs per *day*. Often the weight of the daily total of eggs actually exceeds the weight of the bee herself. It is metabolism carried to extremes.

These reproductive organs consist of the two ovaries which produce the eggs, and a sac called the spermatheca into which the spermatozoa of the male find their way at the time of mating. It is a reservoir for them from which they reach the egg passing out of the vagina, a tiny number at a time, throughout the rest of the lifetime of the queen. Mackensen in 1955 found—and this figure is almost unbelievable—that in the average mated queen this reservoir held 5,730,000 sperm. The only thing more incredible than this huge number of sperm in so small a reservoir in so tiny an insect, is that Mackensen found a way to count them.

The drone has the male organs, but nothing else useful to the cooperative life of the hive. At the time of mating, the male organs, including the sperm sac, are ripped from the body of the successful candidate much as the stinger and sac are ripped from a worker's body when she stings. And like her, he dies.

As for the dozens of drones that flew with the queen and tried to reach her first and failed, they have at best only a few sun-filled days left to them. They have no nectar-gathering equipment. The workers must feed them. This is one reason it is so easy to starve them to death toward winter when they are no longer needed.

As we've seen earlier, the drone has no stinger and so, in spite of his size, can't force his way back into the hive once his worker sisters have decided he is no longer useful. It is, on the whole, the life (and death) of a wastrel; a lazy buzzing-around in the sun, no work, a preoccupation with sex, fed by beautiful women; and then, starvation and death for a reckoning. I'm sure Horatio Alger would have approved.

There are three main races of bees in the United States. They are the German bees, the Italian bees, and the Caucasian bees. In color they are black, yellow, and black with a touch of gray.

Of these three, the Italian bees are by far the most popular. This was, however, not always so. The German bees were at one time widely popular in the United States. The Caucasians have been introduced much more recently than either of the other two, and have made headway slowly.

There are black (sometimes called brown) bees in all the countries of Central Europe, and Germany centers this region. This gave rise to the name German. Actually there are two types of black bees. Philip Baldensperger says that the ones which were imported into America came from Holland, not central Europe, and are very different in their characteristics from the German black bee even though they look much the same. He says our German bees should actually be called Dutch in the interests of accuracy.

At any rate, our United States black bees leave much to be desired from a beekeeper's point of view, which accounts for their gradual decline in popularity. Their worst fault is their inability to fight off a bee disease called European Foul Brood. Both Italian and Caucasian colonies, if infected, fight this disease strongly and often successfully. But not the U.S. variety of German bees. In addition, they have the reputation of being much shorter-tempered than other bees. Some authorities claim that this is not really true. They say it stems from the fact that when a German hive is opened, the bees run in all directions and scramble all over the comb as if they were completely disorganized. If you knock them off the comb onto the ground, they will continue to run in all directions, and this tendency often gets them up under your clothing where they will sting viciously.

To add to the list of their faults, they swarm often, and unexpectedly. Second and third swarms are sometimes given off at such a rate that only the original, or "prime," swarm, survives. Even the mother colony dies that winter, so depleted is it through losing so many of its colony members to swarming. Also, they let the wax moth live in their hives, sometimes to such an extent that the combs are ruined and the colony weakened until it winter kills.

They will also rob other colonies quicker than Italians or Caucasians, and in so doing upset a whole apiary. Too, they will more often hover some six inches in front of the beekeeper's eyes, zigging back and forth, buzzing angrily. They'll stay in that position all day if not destroyed, following him wherever he goes in the apiary. Even inside the safety of a bee veil, this is a most unnerving three- or four-inch rapid zigzag, and one calculated to make the apiary work most unpleasant.

To offset these disadvantages a tiny bit, German bees can be moved short distances easier than Italians because they seem to take note of any slightest change in location, while the Italians note only a major change, go out without taking proper bearings. And so the Italians return, not to the hive, but to the location where it used to be. The Germans, on the other hand, will even fly around and find the new location. Once lost, the Italians are lost completely and do not know how to find themselves.

In addition, German bees cap their honey whiter than any other bee, so that it makes a very fine appearance, especially when sold as comb honey. And at extracting time they are shaken off the combs far more readily than other bees, even though they scramble in all directions when shaken off.

To sum up, then, the German (Dutch) bees of the United States, are not a good race to pick for beekeeping. But the German bees of Germany, Norway, Sweden, Austria, France,

Switzerland, Russia, England, and many other countries are still in favor in those countries.

They do not scramble wildly all over the combs, they are gentle, do not swarm excessively if care is taken, are easily subdued by smoke, and are just as resistant to European Foul Brood as are Italians. They are not imported into the United States because Isle of Wight disease is widespread in the countries where they live, and since they aren't actually better than Italians, beekeepers would be reluctant to take a chance of getting infected bees, even if the United States Government would allow their importation.

Caucasians are black with whitish fuzz on the abdominal bands, so that they can be told from Germans by an expert. But to the layman Caucasians are black and they and Germans look alike. There the resemblance ends, however. They are said by experts to be the gentlest race of bees in the world. Beekeepers take the hives apart again and again without being stung. Caucasians bluff anger. They even fly against the operator's face and hands as if they intended to do big things, but then they return to their combs without using their stingers. They, too, are resistant to European Foul Brood, and they don't scramble all over the combs when the hive is opened, nor do they swarm to excess.

There are, however, two kinds of Caucasians, those from the Caucasus Mountains, and those from the plains regions. Only the mountain bees of this race are gentle.

The Italians are the backbone of beekeeping in the United States. They are gentle, resist European Foul Brood, clean out the wax moth in no time. In fact, if an Italian queen is introduced into a hive where Germans are being attacked and weakened by wax moths, as soon as the young Italian bees begin to hatch out they will clean the wax moths out and save the colony. Root described it: "Lead the worms out of the hives by the ears."

They do not scramble on the combs, are hardy and work hard. They are considered to be among the most beautiful bees in the world. They swarm according to a predictable pattern of behavior, do not do so to excess, and stick rigidly to their pattern.

The Italian bees in the United States usually have three yellow bands. Very yellow bees occasionally have four yellow bands and once in a while even five. In this regard our strains of bees have outdone the original Italians. Those imported from Italy have only two bands of yellow, and it is a much darker yellow than our United States Italians.

The yellow Italians were thought to have originated when Greek sailors, back before Christ, took yellow Cyprian bees with them whenever they went anywhere to stay for any reasonable length of time. The yellow Cyprians crossed with the blacks that were then native to the Italian peninsula, forming the original Italians.

The Roman empire advanced northward, and took the yellow bees with it. The first Italian bees imported into America, came to us in 1855 through a man named Dzierzon, who also gave the world an extremely important theory about bee reproduction.

Bees were shipped direct from Italy to Flushing, New York, and to Philadelphia, Pennsylvania, in 1860. From that time on, importations came more and more often, and the Italian bees already in this country were interbred to give us the race of bees which our vast honey industry depends on so heavily today.

In addition to the three main races, there are the yellow Cyprians which we mentioned above. They're a little smaller than Italians, but are the same color. They probably are the bees from which, originally, all the other yellow bees came. They have miserable dispositions. There are Carniolan bees. There are Syrian bees, Palestinian bees, Egyptian bees, honeybees of India, and even Chinese-Japanese bees. All have drawbacks from a commercial beekeeper's point of view.

But the races of bees all over the world, in general, have their queen, their workers and their drones. They pollinate the plants and trees of the world, and in doing so perform their greatest service to man. Man in turn, by robbing them of their excess stores, brings to his table one of the sweetest, pleasantest, most flavorful foods the world has ever known.

3

---•◆•---

QUEEN LIFE

The main roadblock in the way of the average person's understanding of a queen bee is the word "queen" itself. We think of a queen in terms of the powers and privileges of a human queen. And we take it for granted that a queen bee, because she has that name, has the same powers and privileges. Nothing could be further from the actual facts.

First, we think of a queen as a ruler. We think of her as very rich, beautifully dressed, lying late in bed in the morning, leading a life of ease. We think of her as having her every whim catered to; and doing no work whatever, traveling at will to other areas of the world. We think of her subjects as mourning her lavishly when she dies.

Most of all, we think of a human queen as being feminine; of having every feminine instinct. When, as the result of a royal marriage, she bears children, we think of her as caring for them just the way any other human female would. Her mammary glands are like those of the lowest commoner and she can feed her own child. Fierce mother instinct is present in her, and because of her power as queen, she can and does do more for her offspring than other mothers can. When the queen consort dies, there can be no more offspring until she marries again. She has no control over the sex of her offspring. Many a queen over the centuries would have given much of her worldly possessions to have been able for sure to produce a male child.

The life and status of a queen bee is so fantastically different from this that there ought to be another word for her instead of "queen." It should be a brand-new word, because there is no other state like hers outside the world of insects.

True, her subjects protect her, caress her, vie in their efforts to feed her when she indicates hunger. They surround her and each holds out a drop of nectar on the labellum for her. They show delight by a special movement of the wings when they smell her presence or even smell the spot where she has been recently. They remove her feces and carry this waste outside the hive. They set up an actual wailing when she dies and they find themselves queenless. But about there the resemblance to a human queen ends.

First off, she is not by any stretch of the imagination a ruler as we think of one. She doesn't go around issuing orders and making decisions that have to do with the welfare of the colony. The workers rule.

She has work to do, very important work. If she doesn't do it, the worker bees know it quickly, and they take steps to get rid of her and put a new queen in her place. Her business is the laying of eggs. Her status is no more than that of an egg-laying machine.

There's no lying late in the morning for the queen. She lays instead of lies. There is no finery, no special ease of privilege. She actually leaves the hive area for only two reasons in a lifetime of up to five years; when she takes her mating flights, and when she leaves the hive at swarming time each year. The pampered human queen (and even your own wife for that matter) would roll a head or two if any attempt were made to hold her to a few hours outside the palace once a year. Your wife may at times feel she is imprisoned by household duties, and let you know about it. But even at such times she would feel her lot was far, far better than that of a queen bee.

The death of the drone with whom she mated in no way stops her production of young. I have mentioned already how his sex organs are often torn from his body and remain in the queen. His subsequent death in no way affects her laying of eggs for the rest of her life. And whereas 3,000 eggs per day is pretty well the outside limits of even a prize queen bee, a good one may average, at the height of the honey season when the nectar is coming in rapidly, 1,500 eggs a day. For the whole honeyflow she would conservatively average 1,000 eggs a day. If she didn't, the hive would suffer and the workers or the beekeeper would get rid of her.

Getting rid of her is called superseding if the bees do it, and requeening if the beekeeper does it. Many beekeepers requeen each year; almost all the good ones requeen at least every two years. The queen's egg-laying powers are likely to grow less if she is older than that.

She can, at will, decide the sex of the bee that will be produced when she lays an egg. Just think of that for a moment. It is an incredible thing, hard for humans to realize or believe.

This theory, generally accepted now as fact, was first propounded in 1845 and was called the Dzierzon theory. It was named after Rev. John Dzierzon, a student of bees. It met violent opposition at first, but later some of its enemies became its staunchest supporters. Briefly, the theory was that drones were born from unfertilized eggs. Conversely, Dzierzon believed that any egg that was fertilized produced a female, either developed or undeveloped.

One thing which led him to this theory was that sometimes, when a colony became queenless, and there were no eggs or larvae for the producing of a queen, a laying worker bee would appear with her female organs partly developed. She would begin to produce eggs. This laying worker would be treated by the other workers very much as they would treat a queen. The worker bees would not tolerate a laying worker if they had a queen, or even if there was a substantial hope of their producing one. But when hope was gone, they would.

The eggs laid by such a laying worker in all observed instances produced offspring. But they produced only drone bees, never a queen or worker bee. Since a laying worker was unfertilized, but could produce eggs which would become drone bees, it was no wonder that the next step in Dzierzon's thinking was the decision that drone eggs were unfertilized, female eggs were fertilized. It went against the usual idea that nothing could be produced without fertilization.

The fact that a queen could produce both workers and drones and that for the most part these drone eggs would be laid in larger drone cells led Dzierzon to the conclusion that the queen could make the decision about whether or not the egg would be fertilized. After years of experiments and observations, he decided that when the queen wanted to lay a female egg she flexed muscles which drove an infinitesimal amount of male sperm held in the sac connected to the oviduct, through the tube to meet the egg there and fertilize it.

For years heated conflict swirled around this theory. This

wasn't stilled until a man named Newell, in Houston, Texas, crossed Italian and Carniolan bees. The Italian strain is dominant, and a union of these two will always produce Italians because of that fact. When Newell mated Italian queens with Carniolan drones, the progeny were all Italian. The fact that the Italian strain was dominant accounted for this in the workers and queens produced, and could also account for it in the drones. But in the drones it might also be that they came from an Italian egg unfertilized.

However, when the experiment was reversed, and Carniolan queens were mated with Italian drones, the results were very different. Again the workers and queens produced were Italian because of the dominance of the strain.

But the *drones produced were all gray Carniolans like the mother.* They must, in other words, have been produced from an unfertilized egg, else the dominant Italian strain would have taken over.

At last there was proof of the main premises of the Dzierzon theory. Since then untold hours of work and experimentation have gone on in this field. The theory still stands much as it was originally put forth.

But in one area the experiments and the work have brought to light a very strange, almost unbelievable exception. It is, most scientists believe, the exception that proves the rule.

Various reports came in from time to time that females of some strains of bees had developed from unfertilized eggs. This seemed to account for the occasions when a colony, hopelessly queenless, suddenly, against all the rules, had a queen and were back in business. Scientists wondered if such a thing were possible, if it explained why laying workers appeared and were tolerated at all. Suppose that, all hope for the colony gone, the workers resorted to a last effort against fantastic odds and made queen cells around the eggs of a laying worker. And that sometimes this terrific gamble paid off.

So the scientists isolated virgin queens. These queens would lay eggs. The eggs would produce drones as expected. However, about 0.85 percent of the time a female egg would be produced by some queens of a few strains. Was it too much to believe that against odds far greater than these, the tremendously rare female egg that a laying worker seemed able to produce once in a great while, could be turned into a queen and the hive saved? Many have decided this is at least theoretically possible with some strains of bees.

Still, in spite of this work, if less than one in a hundred female larvae can come from unfertilized eggs—and many of the queens tested could lay no female eggs at all from unfertilized eggs—these parthenogenesis or "virgin development" observations are only fascinating and almost unbelievable exceptions to Dzierzon's rule. Actually, the fact that an unfertilized egg can produce anything at all, even a drone, seems incredible to all of us except scientists who have delved deeply into these matters.

A human queen can feed her offspring. But a queen bee has no organic power to produce the pap, or royal jelly, which is absolutely essential to the development of the larvae. Even if the queen could and did produce the royal jelly, it would be physically impossible for her to do so in quantity sufficient to handle a thousand to fifteen hundred hatching eggs each day.

Actually, the queen seems completely uninterested in the care of her young; her efforts in that department end strictly with the laying of the egg in the cell. All the rest of the work that a mother usually does, and there is a fantastic amount of it, she leaves to the worker bees. The workers can and do produce from their foreheads the glandular brood food, the royal jelly, which all larvae must have for three days. It is a thick, creamy white substance with a smell pungent to human nostrils. And it is a little bitter to our taste. They feed the jelly to the larvae and later feed them bee bread (mixed pollen). They cap the cells, even clean the cells before the egg can be laid in them.

The queen has no wax glands and she therefore cannot even produce for herself the cells in which the eggs must be placed if successful results are to be obtained. Here again she depends on the workers. She won't even defend her young from attackers.

Perhaps, then, it is actually inaccurate to say that a queen is a fully developed female, and a worker is an undeveloped female. "Fully developed" should mean having every organ and instinct necessary for the successful producing and raising of future generations. Yet the queen as we have just seen can neither produce the food for feeding her babies, nor the wax to provide her young with an incubation area.

On the other hand, the workers aren't completely undeveloped any more than their queen is completely developed. In cases of dire extremity they can produce eggs. They and they alone have the organ for producing the necessary royal jelly food. And they alone can produce the wax to make the cells.

Actually, then, brood cannot be raised without the two working in conjunction. Each is partly developed according to the definition above. They supplement each other. However, the terms "developed female" and "undeveloped female" are in universal use, they describe the situation better than any other short descriptive term I can think of, and so we'll continue to use them.

Whereas a queen can produce either drones or workers at will, she can't decide to produce another queen and make the decision stick. Only if the workers cooperate can she carry through this decision. They must build with their wax a larger cell.

Then comes the completely incredible part. She will lay in that cell a fertilized egg which in a regular-sized cell would produce a worker bee. The workers will draw out the cell, they will bustle around it. It will hang down instead of sticking out to the side. On its outside they will produce a regular pattern of indentations which look like tiny hexagonal cell bases. These may be decorations for a royal crib; if so the design is appropriate since the royal grub inside will, if she matures, lay eggs for a lifetime in cells that have this same base pattern.

To the larva which hatches from this egg the workers will feed royal jelly. They won't feed it just for three days, as they feed it to a worker or a drone. They will immerse the little thing in royal jelly. She will eat royal jelly *only* throughout the sixteen days it will take her to come out of her cell a full-grown queen. The worker larvae eat bee bread made of pollen after the first three days.

And therein lies the wonder. Just from this change of diet and from the larger cell she grows in, the tremendous differences in structure and habits come. She will be much larger than a worker, much longer and slimmer than a drone. She will seldom if ever use her stinger on anything but another queen bee. She will have that infinite capacity for laying fertilized eggs. Her sex organs will be highly developed. She will live years where the worker would live weeks, at the most months. She will make no attempt to leave the hive to collect nectar or pollen as a worker does.

When it is time to cap the queen cell, the workers will

put a thick pointed cap on it. When they are finished, the whole thing looks like a peanut; it has the same shape and the tiny indentations.

When the sixteen days are nearly up, the workers will usually come and remove most of this cap, leaving the tiny new life only a thin covering. When she is ready, the queen will gnaw through this with her sharp mandibles. She will turn herself in the cell as she does so, and the resulting cut will look as if it were made with a compass.

Occasionally the workers forget all about partially uncapping the cell, and the queen seems to have no difficulty cutting through the heavier covering. Occasionally, too, before she is ready to come out, she will squeal inside the cell so loudly she can be heard by human ears. Perhaps this is a battle cry for other queens about to hatch out. (She has another, far different cry which she emits at times and which can be heard clear across a room.) But this cry inside the capped cell is distinctive and is heard only before she emerges. She never uses it again.

This is what happens when a queen is born under normal hive procedures, ahead of swarming, or when the old queen is growing too old to function properly. The workers prepare special queen cells, and their old queen lays an egg in them. She does this either because the empty cells are there and she has an inner urge to lay an egg in each empty cell in a given area, or because she realizes that the hive is crowded and needs to swarm or that she herself is over the hill. Who knows for sure? Anyway, she lays the egg, and the workers take over from there.

When, however, something suddenly happens to the queen, or an accident cripples or takes from her the ability to lay eggs, the procedure is very different and even more wonderful.

When the colony becomes queenless and they find it out, there comes from the colony a doleful, despairing buzzing or wailing sound which is upsetting to hear. Queenlessness can mean the extinction of the colony unless something can be done quickly. Bees will die off, their life-span ended; if no new bees are to hatch out, all will be gone in a matter of weeks. This is, for the bees, a terrible calamity, and their wail somehow gets across to the listener the depths of their desperation.

Queenlessness which happens suddenly, almost always finds the bees with eggs recently laid, or larvae only recently hatched out. These will be in ordinary standard worker cells.

The bees will wait for these eggs to hatch, or will pick several larvae already hatched out. They will supply these with extra royal jelly. There will be more than they would give an ordinary worker larva.

Next they will begin to tear out the cells around these chosen larvae. They will destroy and carry away the larvae or eggs in the torn-out cells. They will begin the construction of a queen cell around each of these chosen tiny larvae. Since this takes up the space of about three ordinary cells there will be considerable numbers of young who must die before they are really born, so that their hive may continue. Bees seldom show any compassion for the crippled bee or the maimed or imperfect brood. The continuation of the colony is the one thing they think about, and compassion for a crippled larva or bee doesn't fit within this instinct.

They will pack each new queen cell with royal jelly, will cap it as we have described earlier. The web will be spun inside the cell, the sixteen days will elapse, and if you have the hive open, you can actually hear the queen gnawing to release herself. Soon her sharp mandibles will break through the cover. She keeps exerting pressure on the cap, and usually it will pop open before she has completed her circle of gnawing.

And with her emerging, the hive again has a queen. Long since, the wailing has subsided; it is only a hive newly queenless from which the sound comes. And the news of a new queen seems to pass rapidly through the whole colony. The bees near her move their wings in a particular way which seems with them to indicate joy at being with or near a queen bee.

The first thing the new queen does is move across the combs until she finds an uncapped cell containing honey. She eats what she wants of this, and begins again to crawl about over the combs. She is probably not just exercising her long legs, learning to use her feelers, or examining the sort of world into which she has been born. She is driven on by a much more primitive and basic instinct. She is looking for other queens or queen cells.

She has no intention of bidding another queen welcome if she finds one. She will attack her; they will attack each other. They will fight and one will finally succeed in stinging the other. A queen that has been stung in this way will roll over and die.

If she doesn't find another live queen, if the colony's old queen has already left with a swarm to establish a new colony and no other queens have hatched out ahead of her, she will still be unsatisfied. She will seek out any unhatched queen cells. She will tear into the sides of these with her mandibles, rip a chunk out of each of them. She may sting the soft undeveloped insect inside, or she may only leave the cell open. The workers following her around, true to their instincts, will finish the job. Experimenters have actually removed the unborn queen from a torn-open cell like this, before the workers had done much to it. They have incubated the pupa, and raised a queen minus a wing or leg or whatever part the attacking queen or the workers had already mutiliated or torn from it.

Once the matter of rivals has been taken care of, the new queen will parade around on the combs. She will gradually decrease in size until it is hard to tell her from a worker. She moves around over the combs for about a week, doesn't rest or stop as far as most observers have been able to tell. Just before she's ready to lay eggs she'll be back to her original size, but right now she's smaller.

Sometimes during this period she may utter her other sound, which is like a loud *see-ee-eep, see-eep, seep*. The first note is long, the others not as long. If watched under a reading glass her wings will make a trembling movement while the squeal is being uttered. Older queens don't seem to squeal unless hurt.

The virgin queen now goes to the hive opening more and more often as the days advance. Usually this takes place about the fifth or sixth day of her life. The next day or the next, she will take a short flight for the first time. She will run back and forth, finally take off and be airborne. She will hover above the entrance, probably making careful mental notes on the minutest details of its appearance. She will move farther away, still seemingly getting to know the locale from every angle. She'll light sometimes, and start again, fly and return. All this she'll do in the sunniest part of the day.

She'll take longer and longer flights, at first not going out of sight of the hive, but then either later that day or the next, leaving completely and again returning.

Sometime, usually between the fifth day and the tenth day of her life, she will mate. The visible signs of mating will appear, usually on the second or third flight. Occasionally they will appear after the first flight or as late as the fourth flight.

Scientists examined this phase of bee genesis in as much detail as they could. These experiments were first made possible by putting a queen excluder in the hive opening which, while allowing workers to move back and forth unhindered, would not allow the queen to pass through. When she was seen on the inside of this excluder, it was removed and she was allowed to fly. The opening was always watched for her return. But the only way they could tell whether or not she had mated was from the male organs which remained in her vagina upon her return.

For many years it was thought that queens mated only once. But the experiments described above proved that some queens from some strains mated twice. They flew again after their first successful mating, and returned again sometimes with and sometimes without visible signs of successful mating. Occasionally a queen flew a third and fourth time, but there had been no instances where a third successful mating had surely been accomplished as far as scientists knew until the work of Roger Morse and others at Cornell University.

Dr. Morse wanted some sure method by which the mating of a queen bee could be studied. So he attached a three-foot, very thin monofilament line, using quick-drying glue, to the back of the thorax of a seven- to ten-day-old queen ready to mate. The other end of the monofilament line he attached to a helium-filled balloon. Then he raised this to a height between twenty and one hundred feet above the ground. The queen could fly in a radius of about three feet from the balloon.

With field glasses and from high vantage points he studied the tethered queen. The drones zoomed in upon her in large numbers. She mated with several of them on each flight. Up until these experiments most people had thought she mated with only one drone on each flight.

But drones were not attracted to a queen below fifteen feet. And if she attracted large numbers of drones at a higher elevation and Dr. Morse then pulled her down below the fifteen-foot line, the drones would disperse almost at once.

By raising these tethered queens in different areas, he found, too, that some areas seemed to be congregating areas for large numbers of drones. This was true even though these areas might be further from an apiary than some other area that produced almost no drones. This most-of-the-boys-whistling-at-girls-in-front-of-the-corner-drugstore idea was a new one to apiculture. Dr. Morse was able to take pictures of these swarms of drones around a tethered queen.

These experiments and others convinced him that there must be some strong attractant given off by a queen bee that called the drones to her on her mating flight. In its way it must be much more potent even than Chanel No. 5 used by some lovely young lady on human males. Because if that queen bee flew only one-half mile from home, at heights of from fifteen to seventy-five feet from the ground, the drones would have to locate her in about fifty million cubic yards of flight space. And obviously it wasn't that hard.

So he squashed parts of queens onto small pieces of filter paper which he suspended from a monofilament line stretched between two tall poles. He squashed the mandibular glands, the heads without mandibular glands, the abdomens, and the thoraces; and in every case the drones were attracted rapidly and first to the mandibular gland paper.

The mandibular glands of the queen bee are very large in comparison with those of other hymenoptera. When the mandibular gland lipids were analyzed they contained queen substance (9-oxodec-2-enoic acid). It became apparent, then, that there was a powerful drone-attractant, that it came from the mandibular glands, and that it contained queen substance. The ready-to-mate queen was able to call the drones from great distances with it, and this ability allowed those drones to find her in the vast reaches of space. It allowed her to mate rapidly and return with a minimum of danger from predators that might have caught her had she roamed far and long.

Up until these experiments few people had ever actually seen the mating of a drone and a queen in the air. It happened always high above, where humans weren't able to be except in machines which would chew up the maters. Still, a few observers had had the two bees, locked together, land at their feet. Maeterlinck, many years ago, had such an experience, and describes it at first hand in his *The Life of the Bee*.

There is no way of knowing how the little ladies themselves felt about these infringements of a privacy which had been well-nigh complete for so many centuries. I imagine they were highly outraged and wondered what the world was coming to.

When there are multiple matings they happen within hours of each other; it is never a case of a queen remating weeks, months, or years after her first mating. She mates at one time in her life, and that is it.

Egg laying usually begins between the second and the fourth day after successful mating. From then on this little egg-laying machine goes into high gear and just keeps on and on turning out those tiny, transparent ricelike grains. Only termination of the honeyflow, or cold weather, will slow her down.

Believe it or not, artificial insemination has been practiced on queen bees successfully. Because of the difficulty of controlling the drone that mates with a queen high in the air, some such procedure had to be attempted and perfected to make crossbreeding experiments feasible and reliable. It is, as can be imagined, a very delicate matter, performed under magnification.

Once the mating is over, gadding for the queen is over, too. Her next outside appearance will be at swarming time, which usually won't happen for a year. She is older now, and when queen cells have been capped, she will no longer tear them apart. She will still fight another live queen—two of them placed under a water glass even in the hot sun will still fight to the death—but she will not tear open cells in which her eggs are growing.

Instead, in the normal course of events and if the beekeeper has not taken steps to combat this urge, she will take a large percentage of the workers with her and leave the hive. This is called swarming.

The queen's function in swarming is all-encompassing. The bees may start out, and if the queen doesn't follow they will return, the attempt abortive. Actually, if this happens a couple of times, they may even kill her.

But suppose she does go with them. She is the minute focal point on which everything else depends. When she lights, the workers cling in a fantastic mass dripping with bees. When the scouts report and she flies to the new home, the mass of bees flies with her. And when she enters the new home, the workers enter, begin to build comb, and their hive life starts again. She begins to lay eggs and build up the strength of this new colony until it will be as strong as the colony from which it came.

Swarming will be gone into in detail in another chapter. Suffice it to say here that around the queen the whole undertaking revolves, both figuratively and literally. Without her there can be no swarming.

How do the bees keep track of her in the air during swarming? How do they know she is in the hive during the many uneventful days of the honeyflow, when each of 50,000 bees couldn't possibly keep track of her personally? Again, by that very distinctive odor.

Two odors, actually. First there is the queen odor, which all queens seem to have. It comes from that chemical known as queen substance and this has comparatively recently been isolated by a man named Colin G. Butler, its discoverer. This queen substance which we mentioned above as being produced by the two mandibular glands in the queen's head, comes down onto her mouth parts. It looks like milk. The workers get it by licking the queen's body. In turn it is passed on to other workers in food and in normal hive activities. As long as it is present, the bees know they have a queen. Experimentation has proved that if you give confined queenless workers some queen substance in food and let them smell a queen's odor, this will keep them from building queen cells. More work is being done in this area by scientists who believe that queen substance and other chemicals from the queen may be the means of communicating between queen and workers. The scientists are sure there is some sort of communication, and they think these chemicals may be the answer to what it is.

This queen odor the bees find exciting, irresistible. If you hold a queen bee in your fingers, workers will crawl all over your hand if given the chance, even hours later, and they will give that peculiar shaking of the wings which seems to be their way of indicating queen-induced joy and excitement. Walk around in an apiary after you've handled that queen, and bees will follow you to light on your hand. A queen whose wings have been clipped on one side may fall in the grass; you can tell where she is crawling by the behavior of workers lighting and crawling on the path she took. There'll be a line of bees behind her. Workers will crawl for hours on a spot where a flying queen has momentarily lighted.

If a colony is queenless, the effect is heightened manyfold. They'll go into a sort of ecstasy when they come in contact with that odor. If you take a cage containing a queen and hold it above the colony, the first bees that catch the scent will begin shaking their wings. Leave it, and shortly nearly the whole colony will be hanging to it.

It is assumed by many beemen that this odor which the queen gives off helps keep the swarm together in flight. The swarm falls apart and disintegrates if the queen is not with the bees. How could the bees all know their queen was there except by odor?

There is also the second, or personal, odor which each queen imparts to her own colony. Neither odor is distinguishable to human nostrils; at least not to mine.

The personal odor, as differentiated from the queen odor, is the basis of all hive protection. Each queen evidently smells personally different from any other queen. She imparts this odor to her offspring. The hive itself, full of all these bees with the same odor, is permeated with it. It has become the hive odor.

When robber bees visit a colony, the guards recognize an intruder by her odor which is different from their own. The whole colony system would be completely disrupted without it. It is no exaggeration to say that colony life could not exist. Bees would, if there were no way of telling robbers from the fifty thousand legitimate inmates, rob constantly and be robbed. They would spend so much time stealing and re-stealing that there might be no time to go to the fields for new honey. It would be like humans if there were no moral force and no police. Conceivably we'd all be spending our days, not in production, but in trying to hold what we had or get what somebody else had.

But with the colony odor, the bees know friend from foe. The colony protective system can be set up, and the colony stores safeguarded.

It is this odor which taxes a beekeeper's ingenuity when he wants to requeen. To introduce a queen with a different odor into a hive cold, would cause the workers to "ball" (form a ball of live bees around her and either smother or sting her) and kill her at once.

It will be seen from the above, then, that this amazing little lady is at once the ally and the problem of the beekeeper. And in her case, as in everything else connected with the manipulating of these thousands of insects to his own ends, the beekeeper has experimented constantly through the years. He has taken the need of the workers for their queen, and their ironbound habits with regard to her, and turned them to his advantage.

One way he has done this is with the commercial production of queens in the South to be shipped by mail. Beekeepers who furnish queens make their money, not by selling honey, but by selling bee-egg-laying machines.

Far north in areas of the United States and Canada where winters are so rugged that bees cannot successfully and economically be held over the winter, the beekeepers order packages of bees, each with a queen, in the same number as the total of colonies they intend to run that summer. These arrive in the mail, are given the hives and combs of last summer's bees, providing of course that last summer's were disease-free swarms. The new bees will clean up the combs, get them ready for the eggs and honey, and will be ready to work when the honeyflow starts. A three-pound package of bees with queen will be about the equal of a hive that has wintered over.

A. I. Root, the father of beekeeping in the United States, was the one who first started the shipping of bees in wire cages. He did it so that a hive could be shipped at a low rate, knocked down, and the bees for it shipped later. He probably did not realize the extent to which this related industry would later develop. It was, at first, based on the discovery of a candy for food which was just hard enough but not too hard to carry the bees in good condition to their destination. Not everybody knew how to make this candy, so only those who did, sold bees. Later it was discovered that a can of syrup, properly installed and fixed so that it would ooze out slowly enough to care for the wants of the bees, worked even better. In these packages a caged queen is hung in the center.

But suppose only the queen herself is needed; you have a colony to requeen. Your brood chamber has told you that the laying of eggs in that colony has fallen off badly. The queen-raiser sends you a ridiculously small package which contains only a queen and enough workers to care for her personal needs on the trip. This package is a tiny, reinforced wire cage.

Such a queen carrier can be introduced into the hive at once if the colony has been some time without a queen. The bees will be overjoyed to get it. If their old queen is to be taken from them, though, then the matter is much more difficult.

There are almost as many ways of introducing the queen to her future subjects as there are beekeepers. But the usual way is to have a plug of hard candy in one wall of the cage with a metal tab over it. When the cage is set into the hive, this metal tab is removed. It will take the workers and the queen about three days to eat through this candy once the metal is removed. By that time the colony will have discovered that they are queenless. They will have gotten used to the queen and her retinue through the wire mesh of the box. And when she is free to come out into the hive and start laying, they will ordinarily welcome her and assist her.

The actual raising of the queens is done by the bees. The beekeeper only manipulates. He has queen cups into which he can place larvae. These in turn are given to queenless colonies, or colonies bent on swarming. They will draw these out, feed the tiny larvae, and bring the queens to maturity. However, these cells must be removed from the original hive in time, or they will be torn open and destroyed by the first hatching queen, and the financial loss will be complete. There are many ingenious ways of handling this, but the usually accepted way is to remove the cell before hatching, give it to a small group of bees called a nucleus, and it will hatch among them. Then in many cases the members will be shipped right along with their new queen.

The package bee business has grown from its origin with A. I. Root until now over a million pounds of bees are shipped yearly.

Thus we see that our little lady, though not much of a mother, is a rather fantastic producer. She performs three impossibilities: She has one short mating period and lays fertilized eggs, often more than her weight in eggs in a day, for years. And even more impossible, she can determine the sex of the egg she lays. Third, she can actually produce bees from unfertilized eggs. The hive life revolves around her, yet she is not running it. The tremendous honey industry and all the pollination of crops rest indirectly upon her competent thorax. And a huge industry has sprung up around the production and shipping of the queen herself and her less sexually developed worker sisters. She is, truly, one of the most astonishing creations on the face of the globe.

4

WORKER LIFE

When you begin to examine the life of the worker bee, you run up against more wonders. But the greatest wonder of all is that fifty thousand of these worker individuals can labor together under one roof in harmony for the common good. There will be no shirking and when work is needed in a special area, that work will call together the workers needed to perform it.

Yet all this is accomplished without apparent direction from any boss bee. There is no head to the organization for order giving. There are no subordinates, or even foremen. Worker bees out-Communist the Communists.

A worker bee starts life as an egg in an ordinary hexagonal cell, about five cells to the inch, in the part of the hive called the brood chamber. (The word "brood" is used to cover everything from the egg to the fully developed bee.) The egg is deposited there by the queen, her retinue hovering around her.

First in this process, she carefully examines the inside of the cell to make sure it has been cleaned. Then she places her legs along the edges of the cells next to that one, and backs her abdomen clear to the bottom of the cell. She remains there less than fifteen seconds. The egg stands up in the bottom parallel to the sides like an upside-down light bulb in a socket. It remains that way until just before hatching. Then it lies flat in the bottom of the cell.

The workers, the house bees that are working with the brood, come often, poke their heads into the cell, and look it over. When finally it lies flat on the bottom of the cell, they deposit royal jelly next to it. It's a large amount of jelly compared to the size of the egg. But it's probably less than the head of a pin in actual volume.

The egg then breaks the membranelike shell and the larva is born. Shortly it forms a letter O with itself, its front end actually touching its back end, all in the bottom of the cell.

The workers keep adding more jelly. The larva grows in its little circle until it fills the bottom. At the end of three days the food supply is changed to bee bread and honey, mixed.

The larva lengthens out in the cell when it gets too big to live in the bottom. During this period it gains over *a thousand times* its own weight. It's good that our own food isn't that potent. It then begins to turn, end for end, spinning a web around itself. Some authorities say it turns only a couple of dozen times, but some think it turns more than a hundred times in its web spinning.

Once the web is spun, the grub straightens out on its back, its head toward the entrance of the cell. And from then until it is ready to break through as a bee into the world of the hive, it lies motionless and takes no food at all. The workers cap its cell; this is the pupa stage.

Twenty-one days from the time the queen backed into that cell, the new bee will cut her way out with her mandibules. It takes the egg three days to hatch. The larva stage lasts six

days, and the pupa stage lasts twelve days. The case of the
queen or the drone is different; the queen, as we have seen,
takes only sixteen days to mature from egg to bee, and the
drone takes twenty-four days. The larva sheds its skin five
times during this cycle, and the pupa once more.

The number of times that the tiny new bee in all three
stages is visited, fed, fussed over by worker bees is so great
that it is inconceivable. Believe it or not, these visits add up
to more than thirteen hundred during some days. And the
total of all visits to a single cell, egg to maturity, is in the
neighbor of ten *thousand*. Ten thousand visits from nurses to
raise one tiny bee. There is, according to Dr. E. F. Phillips,
a total time expenditure of four and three-quarter hours. To
me the vastness of this labor for one tiny bee—and remember, as many as a thousand to fifteen hundred may be hatching out in one day—seems completely incredible, just as do
so many happenings in this wonderful world of bees.

After the new bee has emerged from the cell, she looks
around at the world surrounding her, but with extremely
poor eyesight at that stage, and begins to preen herself. She
brushes her tiny coat, combs herself, and just sits. She can
walk, but she is wobbly, and doesn't fly yet. Throw her into
the air and she'll make no attempt to use her wings. She
still has a downy, whitish look.

By the end of the first day she has begun to dip hungrily
into the uncapped honey supply or been fed by other bees.
And about a day after she is born, she starts her life of work
which never stops, except in winter, until she dies.

She begins her working career by cleaning cells to make
them ready for new bees. This she does by licking the inside
of the cell meticulously and carefully. In doing so she evidently leaves an odor, because no queen will enter a cell
which hasn't been licked clean.

This period in our little girl's life lasts for about three days. She doesn't work all the while, however. She sometimes just sits on capped brood and seems to ruminate. Actually, she isn't fit for any other work at that time. She can't fly, so she can't leave the hive. Her organs for the production of royal jelly are not mature until after the third day. There isn't much of anything else but cleaning and nurse work for which she'd be any good.

Once her forehead glands begin to secrete the royal jelly, the new bee begins to feed larvae, one of whom she has herself so recently been. She furnishes royal jelly to both queen cells and ordinary cells. No other bee has told her to do any of the things she does, as far as science now knows. She has seen the work to be done, or perhaps instinct has taken over. The nursing period usually extends to the thirteenth day. After that her royal jelly glands deteriorate.

At that time in her life the young bee is known as a "house bee." She works only inside the hive. Roughly half her life will be spent (in normal honeyflow) as a house bee, and the rest as a "field bee."

After her duties as cleaner-of-cells for brood, of larvae feeding and royal jelly production, she will turn to the repairing of comb. For this she must produce wax. This too is an astonishing process.

The whole world of bees is dependent on wax. It is the material out of which their storage cups are made. Without it there would be no food for winter. It is the material from which the cradles of their young are constructed, and, without these, again there would be no colony.

Beeswax is actually a fatty acid. It is mostly cerotic acid with quite a large amount of palmitic acid and smaller quantities of other ingredients. It is animal wax, and is quite unlike either the wax made as a by-product of petroleum or the vegetable wax scraped from some plants. Production of bees-wax rests exclusively with the worker bee, and is produced in greatest quantities when the honeyflow is greatest. It melts at around 145 degrees Fahrenheit, but it softens enough to ruin the combs at around 115.

As we have seen in examining the structure of the bee, the wax forms in beautiful thin flakes between the fourth and the seventh sections of her abdomen. So when our new bee wants to produce this wax to help with repair or building, she will hang motionless, inside the hive, and the wax will begin to form. When the flakes are large enough to work with, she will scrape off the scales with the joint of one hind leg. She'll stand on three legs while she does it—one hind leg and the two middle legs.

She will then transfer the flakes of wax to the forelegs by moving, almost faster than the eye can follow, her back leg up where the two front legs can get hold of the wax. The wax she then masticates with her mandibles while she holds it with the forelegs. And that back leg may at the same time be bringing forward another scale. It's all sleight-of-foot, and pretty hard to follow.

Once she is satisfied with the consistency of her ball of wax, she will carry it, of all places, under her chin to pre-serve that consistency until she can reach a place where it is needed. In her case she will do repair work with it first, probably until she gets the hang of it. And then she will attack the manufacture of comb. In the chapter on Hive Life we will go into the drawing out of comb more in detail.

The making of wax is by no means her only duty; actually her duties increase. They don't always come in a given order, since there may be an extreme need for one type of work one hour, while another type of work may demand all the talents of all the available house bees some other hour. But she turns her hand, or rather her foot, to every form of hive work at some time during her early life.

If a heavy flow of honey is coming in during the middle of the day, she will meet the field bees at the entrance and relieve them of their nectar load, or pollen load, or propolis load, so that they can go back again to the field. She will pack the pollen—the field bees just kick it off into a cell—will work the nectar a while and place it in cells, and then go back to meet another bee. When the nectar flow begins to slow down late in the afternoon she may return again to the drawing out of comb.

She will clean house, possibly before the honeyflow starts in the early morning hours. In doing this she will carry out dead bees if there are any, the feces of the queen, wax moths that have been stung to death.

If something needs sticking to something else, she will help unload a bee which has brought in propolis, the wonderful bee glue, and will help apply it where it should go.

And finally she will guard the entrance. In this work she will have to be alert to detect any odor or behavior on the part of a bee different from the hive odor or natural behavior. She will have to be on guard against encroaching ants, mice, snails or any other intruders. She must kill them if any insist on entering. One investigator actually watched one marked bee that remained on guard duty for three full days.

If there comes a time when the temperature inside the hive becomes dangerously high, she will go with the hive bees to the entrance. They will stand there, humped a little in the rear, moving their wings so fast that it is impossible to see those wings. They will be fanning the air for ventilation. Again in Hive Life we will examine this amazing performance more fully.

All these things our house bee will do during her three weeks as a house bee. In addition she may or may not be one who will attend the queen in her egg-laying routine, and hold food out to the queen on her labellum. If she does make this a part of her routine, there will be a very peculiar thing about it. She and the others so engaged will face the queen at all times. They will ring her, their heads toward her. They will act toward her the way attendants are supposed to act toward human royalty, never turning their backs to her.

Since bees antedate human royalty by millions of years, it's not unreasonable to conjecture that human royalty may have picked up the idea from the way a queen bee is treated by her subjects. It's probably not too realistic to suppose that this habit stems from reverence as much as from an attempt to keep plenty of food for the queen's use on plenty of mouth parts facing her all the while.

With thousands of bees moving inside the hive it has not been an easy task for scientists to determine at what age various bees performed various tasks. For a while the new-born bee remains downy-looking, and that helped some. Then some ingenious experimenter placed one section of Italian brood, about ready to hatch out, in a German colony. The yellow bees among all those black ones, were easy to spot and keep track of in the glass observation hive.

Even that, though, didn't allow the investigators to follow one or two bees for several weeks. This was accomplished by marking the bees with a quick-drying paint especially designed for the purpose. This would be dabbed on the thorax of the bee in various colors to distinguish one marked bee from another. It was through the use of these marking devices that the information on the house-bee days of a honeybee was laboriously garnered.

Along toward the end of the nursing period in our young bee's life, she goes out and experiments and learns to fly. She takes short orientation flights, at first *very* short. She must examine everything around the outside of the hive and note it in her mind scrupulously, so that she can return safely. At first the flight is little more than long enough to rid herself of her own feces away from the hive area. But she soon takes longer flights. When she is on cleaning detail, she must fly a little distance out from the hive with whatever debris she is removing.

Then, roughly three weeks from birth, she changes from a house bee to a field bee. In certain unusual hive conditions, when there are not enough field bees, this change has been known to take place as early as the ninth day. And on occasion the bee has gone as much as three days over the usual three weeks before taking to the field.

The field bee collects nectar, pollen and propolis. As far as is known, there is no order in which these jobs are undertaken, as is the case with the cleaning and nursing jobs earlier in the bee's life. A few marked bees were never seen to collect pollen in their whole lives.

As far as is known, young bees don't make their first flight for nectar as the result of watching any communication dance. Possibly, until they have been working in the field a while, they do not understand how to interpret these dances put on by their sisters to tell where nectar is abundant. They may have to be schooled in some mysterious way in the meaning of the dance. At any rate, no marked bees in the experiments that have been written up, ever started out on their maiden foraging trips as the result of watching a dance. Those communication dances, incidentally, will be covered in a chapter all to themselves.

There must be a tremendous amount for our small bee to

learn when first she starts foraging. By circling she must learn her landmarks so that she can return. She undoubtedly has problems with her first load of pollen, her first trip after nectar.

She must learn how to fly in a high wind, how to avoid dragonflies and kingbirds. She must learn how to interpret and then to follow the instructions of the commuication dance. And later she must learn how to dance it for others. Are these matters instinctive, or does she learn by observing? Or is there some form of communication not yet discovered by humans, bee language that allows an older worker to tell a new worker the facts of honey gathering?

Our girl must fly home sometime in her first rainstorm. Some raindrops must be the size of her whole body. We would be stunned even on the ground to be hit by a volume of water as big as we are.

She must find herself tangled for the first time in a spider web, we'll hope not completely. She may run up against men or animals intent on robbing her, and she must decide whether the depredation is serious enough so that she should sting in defense of her home and in so doing give up her own life.

She has a great deal to learn, and all this experience must be telescoped into about three weeks. Her foraging life is only that long in the height of the honeyflow as compared with our "threescore years and ten." Minutes in her life are like days are with us.

Mr. Allen Latham, one of our country's foremost authorities on bees and bee behavior, says that when a bee reaches the prime of life, she becomes a "control bee." These bees are the ones who rule the hive and the queen. They are strong, vigorous, healthy, and able to handle situations that arise. The older bees are growing feeble. The young bees can't fly, some have barely started foraging. But the prime bees can and do rule.

They decide when a swarm is to issue, and many of them go with it. In years past it was thought that the young bees stayed, the old bees went with the swarm. But this does not stand up under observation. There must be field bees remaining with the old swarm, else nothing could be brought in from the field for some weeks. Latham feels that the older field bees remain, the control bees in the prime of life go.

When the queen fails, it is the control bees among the workers who decide that she must be superseded. They make the new queen cells. And when the new queen hatches, if the old one can still lay eggs, the control bees once in a great while may still tolerate her. She may lay right beside the new queen in a heavy honeyflow. And she must know she is growing useless because she won't attack the new queen. Maybe she only knows she'd be beaten in a fight. But once she has outlived her usefulness to the hive, and certainly before winter, the control bees will "ball" her.

This is a death reserved only for queen bees. The workers form a heavy ball around her and remain in that ball until death comes to the queen. It is held by some beemen that the workers smother the queen in this way, or even tear her apart. Others feel that in the ball they sting her to death. The fact that no stinger is ever found in her body is not conclusive proof that they don't. These observers feel that her body is so soft that the barbs in the worker stinger would not be caught and held and the stinger pulled out.

But whatever the method, death is just as inexorable when the balling is done for this purpose. The doomed queen cannot escape it. And our bee, when she is old enough and strong enough to be a control bee, may be one of those who end their queen in that manner.

If the beekeeper happens to be there when the act of balling takes place—and often this is performed when something unusual or disturbing happens to trigger it, like the mere opening of the hive—there are a number of things he can do. He can spray the ball of bees with sugar water. If this liquid penetrates deep enough, the bees will all stop their balling efforts and start cleaning themselves. He can blow smoke on the ball, and it will likely begin to disintegrate. But the most effective way is to throw the ball into water. The bees will leave the queen then, and it is no trick for the beekeeper to save her and dry her out.

However, there isn't much use in saving her if she is an old queen being balled for poor performance of duty. They'll only ball her again. These methods of saving the queen are usually used by a beekeeper who has prematurely tried to introduce a new queen to a hive, and has seen her balled. If he can save her, he can then take new steps to introduce her which may meet with better success. Good queens are expensive.

Balling the queen can also be for her protection, according to some authorities. They claim to have proved that when danger to the hive threatens, they will ball her, and she will come from the ball unharmed. But personally I have never seen any but lethal intent on the part of ballers. It usually starts with one or two bees who have decided the queen doesn't belong to their hive, or isn't laying enough if she is theirs. Our bee could be the one who makes such a decision. Some bee has to make it.

This bee follows the queen around in anger. This evidently crystallizes a latent discontent on the part of others.

Two or three more join the parade. Suddenly there are dozens and hundreds. And the queen is dead.

A heartless matter? It certainly is. But, as I've mentioned before, a colony of bees is heartless, caring only about the welfare of the colony and never the welfare of the individual as distinct from colony welfare. If a defective or crippled bee pushed outdoors by the other bees attempts to come back in, one of the control bees will pick it up, fly perhaps half a mile from the hive and drop it there to die.

So the control bees in the prime of life run the colony. The young and the old bees seem to accept this as a fact of life, and make no effort to contest it.

Bees are much like human beings in many ways, and among them there are delinquents and robbers just as there are among humans. Just as a shady character in the world of humans may have a furtive, evil look, so it is, too, in the world of bees. The robber bee looks greasy, doesn't have much hair, and has a furtive approach to the hive she wants to rob, her legs held at a peculiar angle as if she wanted to be able to use them instantly.

The robber or delinquent bee gets her start in crime much as a delinquent human does. She may have found during a poor honey-gathering period that she must visit over a hundred clover heads to get a load; she must take more than an hour and possibly as much as two, just in getting that one load. So, starting out one time, she may have passed near a neighboring hive and seen a crack at the back where the wood had checked or the nails sprung. She stopped to investigate, possibly after smelling the wonderful odor of honey, and she managed to crawl in through the hole to take what didn't belong to her.

Let's say she got away with it. She probably had difficulty getting out through the crack because she'd filled herself so full. But she managed it. She flew home with her load, came back again to the hole in the neighboring hive. Crawling in and out of that hole wore the fuzz off her body, began to give her the greasy look of a robber bee.

Let's suppose that the beekeeper, too, discovered the hole in the neighboring hive, and covered it. Does our bee go back to the fields for nectar? Not at all. She's tasted the easy robber's life, and she'll never be any good as a collector of nectar again. She spends her time crawling into cracks in other hives, or in trying to. More fuzz is worn off; the greasy appearance becomes more pronounced.

She can't find another fine setup like the first one. Still, she won't work. She finally approaches a hive that seems poorly guarded, from the front. She displays that furtive air, knowing she has no business there, with her legs at a peculiar angle ready for use.

The swarm is weak, the guards are busy and she gets safely inside the hive. She finds an uncapped cell in a spot where there aren't many other bees, and she fills herself. Now comes the test. Can she get out again?

She comes out looking extra plump because of the load she carries. And she can't take off from the low alighting board of the hive. She has to crawl up the side of the hive, launch herself from there. And when she does, her line of flight, due to the weight, will sag dangerously close to the ground before she can get control and be beyond danger.

Sooner or later she's going to be caught and killed. Or possibly, instead, she'll infect a whole colony. Her sisters will go with her and rob the weak swarm she has been robbing. They may fight, and may destroy the true owners of the store of honey. If they win, they'll transfer the honey to their own hive. But other colonies will see and arrive. Robbing will set a whole apiary in an uproar. The bees will sting anyone who gets near them. Small weak hives will suffer.

Robbing is never a beekeeper's problem when there is plenty of nectar in the fields. It is only when the honeyflow stops that robbing—not individual cases of delinquent bees, but robbing on an apiary-wide scale—will get started. The best way to guard against it is to see that the bees have no chance to get a taste of honey. Put screens on honey-house doors and windows. If bees are caught in a honey house, destroy them rather than let them go out and infect others. Watch for cracks and crevices in hives. And as soon as the honeyflow slows down, cut the size of the openings in all hives; they won't need as much room for their entering bees now, and they can defend the smaller opening much more efficiently.

Our bee in the prime of her life is one of the control bees. In the honeyflow she works from dawn to darkness. If the hive's take has been great during the day, there will be a deep, buzzing hum of activity at night. It is a contented roar. The bees have brought in a lot of nectar, and they are working inside during the hours of darkness, fanning, curing the nectar, evaporating the moisture from it. If you hold the flame of a cigarette lighter in front of their entrance, it will show that the air on one side is moving out, the air on the other side is moving in. Our girl is not only working all day in the field, she is working at night, too.

At times when the honeyflow is not great, and the bees can process it as it comes in, the colony goes into a sort of comatose state at night, somewhat resembling sleep. If you disturb them at that time, dump whole handfuls of them into a pail, you won't get anywhere near the reaction you would in the daytime. With a really mild swarm you may get little reaction; they may stay right there, grumpy and sleepy.

In addition to her rest at night, our girl will often crawl

into an empty cell and sleep for half an hour or so after returning from a field trip. At such a time the pulse of her
abdomen slows until it almost stops. When she finishes her
nap she will back out of the cell, comb her head a few times,
much the way a human sits on the edge of the bed and
scratches his head for a while when he wakens. And then, as
if she is conscious of having been lazy too long, she will start
out again in a rush. Occasionally when the honeyflow is
very weak, she will unload and then just sit around on the
combs for possibly half a day doing nothing. This in spite
of her "busy bee" image.

But when the honeyflow is at its height, she rises to the
occasion. She still takes those half-hour naps in an empty
cell, naps she evidently needs to keep going, much as we
must have sleep no matter how busy we are. The half-day
lolling on the combs, though, is by then a thing of the past.
She comes in, stays only a few moments, and starts out again.
And instead of a quiescent time at night, part of her night
must be spent in evaporating the water from the huge flow
of nectar which she has helped bring in during the day.

She works harder and harder, makes more and more trips
to the fields. And, literally, she works herself to death.

That sounds very dramatic, but it is the absolute truth.
In the winter, when the colony is not collecting nectar and
is inside the hive in a huge mass engaged only in trying to
stay alive against zero conditions outside, our bee will probably live from October or November clear through until
spring. She may live even longer.

But when she is working furiously in the honeyflow, her
life expectancy will be only about six weeks. If those two
facts don't add up to working herself to death, nothing does.

She will go to the fields over and over again, return with
huge loads of nectar. If a human carried a load that heavy

in comparison to his size, day after day, it would tax the very strongest of us, even on land. And here the bee must beat those wings of hers fast enough to hold her weight and the weight of the load in the air, and move it swiftly home. Her wings will beat and beat the air in good weather, in storms, with the wind, against it. And literally, those wings will wear out. They will become frayed and travel-worn. In a heavy honey flow, many ragged-winged individuals, loaded with nectar, will alight clumsily and with difficulty and make their way inside the hive to unload. But each day, in a colony where fifteen hundred bees are being born, a comparable number must end their life of usefulness to the colony.

Examine the ground outside the colony on any night during a heavy flow, and you'll find old, tired, dilapidated-winged workers crawling away to die. Experimenters have picked these individuals up, placed them over and over again on the alighting board directly before the entrance. Instead of trying to enter, they seem to know their usefulness is at an end and they crawl back toward the edge of the board, fall off onto the ground and again start their lonely trip away from their hive to die. They are moving far enough away so that some worker won't have to spend precious seconds carrying out a body. The last little effort at selfless service to their colony.

There aren't, on any given day, any such mass of dying bees in front of a hive as a thousand or fifteen hundred would make. So the implication is clear that death comes most often while the bee is making her last determined effort. She has started one more trip to the field. She could do this because she was light and without a nectar load. She once more loads herself. And then she is blown to the ground, or her wings fail her completely with that load and, far from home, still trying, she lies there no longer able to fly, and she perishes.

So our bee reaches a rather pathetic end to a life of selfless communal labor for her colony. It hasn't, possibly, been a bad life. There must have been joyous minutes of flight. There must have been triumphs of nectar sources discovered, of dangers avoided, of predators circumvented. There must have been many sun-filled days of working among beautiful and sweet-smelling blossoms.

And the final triumph, as she dies, must be the knowledge that she has accomplished the end she worked so hard to accomplish. She is leaving her colony strong with the strength of younger bees that have followed her. And rich in stores for the fight against winter, some of which she herself has brought in.

Probably she doesn't think of these things. Possibly she does. Who can fathom the last thoughts in the tiny mind of a bee that has worked herself to death for her colony?

5

SWARMING

In the early days of our country, a man traveling in the farm areas by buggy, sometimes heard from a farmyard a tremendous clatter. When he came close enough he would see the womenfolk and the children in the yard, banging enthusiastically with big spoons on pans. The din was likely to be terrific.

And all this was connected with beekeeping, believe it or not. In those days beekeepers thought that when bees emerged from the hive in the act of swarming, the battering of tinwear would cause them to light and cluster. Then the oldest boy could run and bring his father from the fields to hive them before they absconded and were lost to the farm.

It has been pretty thoroughly proved in later years that all that denting of kitchenwear and damage to eardrums was for nothing. Bees just don't cluster for that reason.

But swarming is something else again. Swarming is as old as honeybees. It is with us today, and it will be with us tomorrow. Science has made some progress in finding out its symptoms, even its causes. Beekeepers have even made some progress in the prevention of swarming. But no positive cure has developed. Just when a beekeeper thinks he has the situation beautifully in hand, his bees will emerge and swarm.

Swarming is a natural instinct of bees. It is the colony's reproductive urge. The colony divides and makes two, much the way, in lower life, an amoeba divides and makes two. If this were all there was to it, a beekeeper would start with one colony, have two by the end of the year, and in twelve years would have 4,096 colonies. This would be a pretty spectacular deal and the world would be overrun with bees and honey in short order.

But calm yourself; there's no cause for worry. It doesn't work quite that way. Colonies are exterminated by diseases and enemies, they winter-kill (often because they are too weakened by swarming to come through successfully), and in other ways the balance is kept.

The term "a swarm of bees" is used to describe the bees and their queen from the time they emerge from the original hive in the act of swarming until they are housed in a new home of their own. After that they become a "colony." Swarming is a natural phenomenon; "swarming-out," however, describes an entire colony coming out and absconding, usually because of disease or other intolerable conditions in their hive or tree, and moving en masse somewhere else.

In the spring a colony that has wintered reasonably well begins to produce brood in anticipation of the honeyflow. There are no halfway measures in this regard, under normal conditions, and there shouldn't be. The colony will produce brood up to the limit of the brood space available, or the capacity of the queen to lay eggs, whichever comes first. At first they produce only worker brood. But as days pass they begin to add drone brood, the first symptom of the possibility that they may swarm.

Then they may begin several queen cells. When eggs are placed in these queen cells, it is a very definite sign the colony intends to swarm. The drone bees were raised to mate with these new queens.

There are other signs that swarming is imminent. There will very often be a lessening of field work with only a trickle of bees coming and going. This is not a sure sign by any means. It may be caused by some natural phenomenon like a delay in the start of the honeyflow.

But if the beekeeper opens the hive and finds that his bees are packed inside, even up in the supers—the extra stories placed atop the main hive by the beekeeper—and that they all look big, then that's a definite sign, when coupled with queen cells, that it won't be long now. The big look to the bees is because each has filled herself with honey in preparation for the swarming. The honey will be used to produce the wax to start the colony off at its new location, and in other ways to get it established.

About the eighth or ninth day after the queen cells are filled and about the time the first of those cells is ready for capping, the swarm will emerge. As we have seen before, the control bees make the decision, not the queen, and most of them go with the new swarm.

The exact time the swarm will emerge is dependent to a great extent on the weather. If it's raining, and the rain lasts several days, the chances of the swarm emerging before the rain is over are practically nil. If it is very hot, the waiting bees, full of honey and ready to go, become most uncomfortable. Often they'll cluster on the front of the hive; conditions inside are just too crowded and unpleasant. The colony is very excited at the prospect of the great event to come. Thus the hot weather may start the swarm-out even before the queen cells are capped. The bees are so crazy to be gone that they no longer give proper consideration to the need for a queen on the part of the old colony.

They come out in tremendous volume and they circle the area while more pour out. The air is filled with bees, literally thousands of bees. There is a feeling of excitement in the whole apiary, and even the other hives seem to catch the excitement. On a warm day more bees will join the swarm than on a cold day.

They fly in tighter and tighter circles, and usually settle somewhere on a tree limb. Definitely, though, it doesn't have to be a tree limb. Bees in the past have lit on pretty near everything from electrical entrances to beekeepers. If the queen is with the cluster, the cluster will hold and grow. It will be a huge, seething, dripping, shape-changing mass of bees, wonderful to see.

Occasionally, for some reason, the queen will not join the bees, and the cluster will break up and return to the hive to find out what is wrong.

Usually, though, she will emerge from the hive after about half the bees have started out. This again, isn't a rule, since sometimes the queen will be among the first to emerge. Usually the bees will cluster nearby, but there again these little insects and their queen refuse to go through any of this swarming routine according to any set rule or pattern, and occasionally they will whirl with a great humming for half a mile or more before they cluster. Or occasionally, Latham says, they will go without clustering directly to a new home which scouts have evidently picked out long before the swarm emerged.

If they cluster nearby, the cluster may remain where it is for anywhere from fifteen minutes to several days, in very extreme cases. Scouts are sent out or, according to some authorities (among them Latham) have been sent out earlier. The scouts are on the lookout for the perfect home; they'll settle for the best one available to them.

Von Frisch, at the University of Munich, says that the scouts do their "wagging" dance when they return to the cluster, the same dance which they do inside the hive to tell their sisters where a new source of nectar is to be found.

Von Frisch has proved that when the scouts return to report, they dance for whatever discovery they have made. And their excitement is in direct proportion to the mental misgivings they have in regard to their find. If it is adequate and that is all, the dance is done pretty listlessly. If it is perfect—a hive with comb all drawn out, everything new and clean and ready for them—the dance will be done with great enthusiasm.

Then a peculiar thing happens. Other control bees in the cluster, go to examine that place or even several places. These will be the ones being danced for with the most enthusiasm. They like the convenience and location of one, particularly, and they return and dance for it along with others already doing so. Scouts doing a halfhearted dance desist and go to see the place everybody is so pleased about. They can tell at a glance that it's better than the old hollow tree full of rot that they themselves found, so they return and add their enthusiastic dance for this place to the growing number of bees dancing for it.

As the other dances stop and the bees doing them return after seeing that better spot, the dancing for the one becomes nearly unanimous.

Sometime at about this stage in the proceedings, the colony, queen and all, will take off and fly to the new home and set up housekeeping. They have their honey in their honey stomachs. They will go at once to the making of comb. The queen will begin to lay eggs in the cells as fast as they are ready, and the new colony will be launched.

Sometimes, Von Frisch tells us, two places are so nearly equal in attractiveness from a bee's point of view, that it will take longer to reach a decision. There was one case he ran into where the choice narrowed down to two places. But these were evidently so nearly identical in their bee appeal that about half the dancing bees were extremely enthusiastic about one of the spots, and about the same number were just as enthusiastic about the other. One group didn't keep gaining from the other as would normally be the case. Each group kept on dancing stubbornly for the one it liked best. They remained several days there, and then from hunger and other causes the cluster began to disintegrate. They never did go to either place, and the swarm was lost.

That is swarming as it takes place without interference from the beekeeper. It may occur any time during the swarming season, the calendar dates of which, of course, vary greatly among different areas of our country because of the tremendous temperature variations. A rule of thumb is that the earlier it takes place, the better the chances are that the new colony and the old one will each be able to build back up to full strength and will be able to gather enough stores to winter. Ideally, it comes when the colony is at its greatest numerical strength, and before the main honeyflow. In my own state of Vermont, which has a late spring, there was a poem in agricultural circles when I was a boy, which dealt with the best time for swarming there. It went:

> A swarm of bees in May
> Is worth a load of hay.
> A swarm of bees in June

Is worth a silver spoon.
A swarm of bees in July
Ain't worth a fly.

In July, the theory was, there would not be time or honey-flow enough left to save the new colony.

Usually the swarming season takes place within a two- to six-week period. Normally bees won't swarm under any cir-cumstances when the honeyflow dries up. They seem to know that to do so would be suicide.

There is no more dramatic or exciting event in the whole of the world of nature than a swarming colony of bees on the move. By many it is completely misunderstood; they are frightened and run for safety when suddenly there is the wild humming and the air all about them is choked with bees. If you are caught in such a situation, bees will swirl around you, even bump against you.

It is an exciting event to witness. And in spite of the lay-man's fears, those bees are not in the least interested in sting-ing; they are experiencing one of the high points of their life as bees, and stinging is the farthest thing from their thoughts.

The causes of swarming? The main one is the instinct to propagate and increase. Crowding seems to come next. There is the tremendous pre-honeyflow increase in the brood nest. Bees are hatching, there is no space for more egg laying, workers tending the bees are crawling all over the brood caring for it—remember those 10,000 visits to a single cell—and there just isn't room enough for everything.

But crowding in the brood nest is not the only crowding that can have its effect on the tendency to swarm. Crowding in the supers can also be a factor. When there is too little room for honey storage, the bees see the honeyflow coming with no place to put it. They get worried, if a bee can be said to worry, and the decision to swarm is born.

If there isn't enough ventilation, bees are pushed toward swarming. And, partly connected with this, if the temperature is high, bees are unhappy and may swarm. A small honeyflow ahead of the main honeyflow can start them off. But once a honeyflow reaches its height, swarming cuts right off. This would lead to the belief that when bees are really doing business, and are frantically immersed in handling it, like humans, they are much too busy to plan trouble.

Probably every beekeeper who ever handled more than one or two colonies for any length of time, has come up with his own theory on how to cope with swarming to his advantage. If not his own theory, his own variation on somebody else's theory. Mainly, though, the idea seems to be, first, to breed away from swarming. If a beekeeper uses only extra queen cells from colonies bent on swarming to requeen his hives, those colonies theoretically would be more inclined to swarm than a colony queened by a little lady whose colony had a record for not swarming much, and whose cell had been produced because of the supersedure motive and not the swarming motive. This isn't going to get you completely away from swarming. But, conversely, using only queens from swarming colonies could, in a few generations, get you an apiary that would become one gigantic swarming problem. Many beekeepers feel that breeding against swarming helps.

Then the next tendency is to try in every way possible to remove the causes that may trigger a decision to swarm. The first and greatest of these is overcrowding.

Beekeepers have a number of methods for combating this evil. The one most generally in use is the double brood chamber. Briefly, this means giving a colony two brood chambers instead of one. Then there's all the egg-laying room any queen could possibly need.

In the mechanics of this, the most universally accepted method is to give the colony a full chamber of honey-filled comb above the main chamber of the hive. They will then have plenty of honey to winter, and, even more important, will have honey enough to keep them a vigorous colony in the spring, before nectar can be brought in from the fields. As the cells of the food chamber up above are emptied, they become available for brood raising in the spring. This is a pretty simple and automatic setup. At the time when the colony needs the empty space for brood the most, the most cells become empty and are ready.

There are infinite variations. Beekeepers put some of the brood upstairs, some of the honey frames in the middle of the brood area, and with as many different ideas in mind as there are beekeepers. Some have even tried swapping and putting the honey chamber with its empty cells down below and the brood chamber above partway through the spring. Some put a queen excluder between the lower brood chamber and the honey chamber when the colony nears its peak strength, and then put the sealed brood up above and the empty cells and unsealed brood down below. The young bees up above hatch out, but do not crowd the brood chamber below in doing so; they're up out of the way. As the capped brood hatches, the cells can be filled with honey. It makes the lower brood chamber as uncluttered as if the colony had swarmed.

Beekeepers have been ingenious, and the sum total of their effort has been to have an uncrowded brood area, and in so doing remove any need to swarm.

The other form of crowding, the bees' fear that the honey-flow will catch them with no place to store it, is very simply taken care of. An empty super, added before there seems to be any real need for it, will handle this swarm-inciting irritant very neatly. The reason this isn't always done is plain carelessness, or failure to realize that when the bees are bringing in unripened nectar, they will put only a small amount of it in each cell even though many cells are only partly filled. Water evaporates from it better this way. It will stay in place, uncapped, through capillary attraction. So even when there is a whole super of only partially filled cells, the bees may still want more space for curing more nectar.

As for lack of ventilation and high temperatures, shade for the hive can be furnished. This should have been done in locating the hive or apiary in the beginning. But if it wasn't, and a sun load seems to be a problem day after day, wooden stakes driven into the ground and wire stretched between them, with branches woven very loosely into the wires, will provide shade.

When the honeyflow starts, anything you have used to cut down temporarily the entrance to make the hive easier to guard should be removed. The wide entrance will make it so much easier for the fanners to ventilate the hive that this may be enough to reduce the temperature. But if it doesn't seem to be, beekeepers raise the hive away from the bottom board with small blocks of wood at each of the four corners. This gives an entrance on all four sides, and will cure almost any ventilation problem. It also speeds matters up when the nectar is flowing into the hive with its tremendous stream of bees. The bees will mostly enter by the regular entrance, but will often leave again on any side where they happen to be when they are ready to return to the field. If this were to be done when there was not a heavy honeyflow, it would be a flag-waving invitation to robbery. But in a heavy honeyflow, bees are seldom much given to robbing. When the honeyflow slows, the weather usually cools a bit and the swarming season is over. The blocks can then be removed and even the entrance cut down in size.

Those are the basic ways in which beemen try to prevent swarming. There are many others or combinations of others. Since new queen cells are essential to swarming, some beemen in the past have sought out and destroyed the new queen cells. But this must be done every five days or so, and is just too much work for a commercial beekeeper. And if even one is missed—and it may very well be—then the beeman will be faced with a swarm emerging unexpectedly. Destroying cells doesn't work too well because the bees will keep replacing these cells as fast as they are destroyed, if the causes of their swarming urge are not done away with, too.

Another plan which was used for a while by beemen was to cage the old queen in the hive, in conjunction with the destruction of all new queen cells. But the colonies did so much less work and were so much more listless without a queen vigorously laying, that all the good done in keeping the colony together was canceled out. Later on, for the number of days that the beekeeper had kept the queen caged, there would be no new bees emerging from the brood. This would weaken the colony appreciably.

On the "if-you-can't-lick-'em-join-'em" theory, some beemen divide a colony artificially that is bent on swarming. This is simply a means of doing the job when and how the beekeeper wants it done, at his convenience, not at the bees' convenience. It should be attempted only near the middle of a pleasant day.

Beekeepers take a few brood comb sections, one of them with the old queen on it, and place them in a new hive. They fill the remainder of the brood chamber of the new hive with empty comb, or with frames that have full starter sheets (pressed wax sheets inserted in frames to guide the workers) ready for drawing out. Then the owner studies carefully the division of bees between the old and the new colony. He then shakes bees from the frames of the old colony into the new hive, until the two are fairly equal. In doing this he keeps always in mind that the field bees away at the time will of course return to the hive left on the old stand.

He now has two colonies, one with a queen, as if it had swarmed of its own accord, and one with queen cells growing. From there on, matters should progress just as if the bees and not the beekeeper had planned it.

Where there is a late honeyflow, the colonies are likely to reach their peak of population too early. In such a case, dividing the colony as I've described works particularly well, and not only gives two colonies instead of one, but often gives as much surplus honey from each as the original would have made if left alone. The bees spend the time between peak and honeyflow producing still more brood instead of doing nothing.

If, however, the colony reaches its peak just as the honeyflow is starting, all possible methods for the prevention of swarming should be tried, because neither the new nor the old colony will have time to build up to strength before they must collect the bulk of their nectar. Even if there is time before honeyflow for both colonies to build back up to maximum strength, dividing should be attempted only with strong colonies that have wintered well.

If a colony decides to swarm even in spite of the efforts of the beekeeper to remove the stimuli for swarming, he has one trick up his sleeve for making sure the new swarm doesn't get away from him. He clips the wings of the old queen on one side of her body. Holding her gently he cuts off the tips of her wings on that side, and after that she just isn't going anywhere with a swarm.

She may emerge with the other bees to try to swarm. But she will be unable to fly. She will usually be found on the ground in front of the hive. Once found, she can be picked up and set upon the alighting board of the new hive which the beekeeper has made ready. The swarming bees will get her scent, will crawl into the hive after her, and the job is done. If the bees have already clustered, the cluster can be shaken in front of the new hive or into it, and when the bees find their queen there ahead of them, they will usually start housekeeping contentedly.

If all attempts to prevent swarming fail and the bees come out anyway with an unclipped queen, the problem they present the beekeeper then is very different. He can't, in most cases, afford to lose them. There goes half of one of his prized possessions. What must he do to keep this potentially valuable chattel from taking up its abode in a hollow tree somewhere in the forest, and being thereby lost to him forever?

First, he can have equipment prepared and be ready to use it when the emergency arises. He should have at least one empty hive always standing ready in swarming season, with comb inside, or a combination of empty comb and frames with full starter sheets. He should have nearby a couple of ladders; a tall stepladder and a regular ladder. He should have a soft brush, a bushel basket, a cheesecloth bag (or a burlap bag, if the weave is loose enough to let through plenty of air) and a long pole with a hoop on the end. He needs a pair of pruning shears. If he happens to have one of those limb cutters mounted on a pole, which line crews and orchard men use, it will sometimes come in handy. He needs a ball of string. There are other items that might be helpful, but those I have mentioned will handle most situations.

If the swarm clusters on a nearby limb, fairly low down, that is the easiest problem of all. The beekeeper can cut off the limb and carry it carefully, bees and all, to the hive. He'll lay the limb down in front of the hive, and then, with his glove or the brush, nudge some of the bees in at the entrance. When they see what a fine home they have here, they'll somehow call their comrades. Nobody knows for sure how it's done, but most beemen think it must be done with scent from those scent glands not much above the base of the worker's stinger. Those are opened wide and scent squeezed from them. And the bees stand there humped up and fan the scent for all to smell. It's like saying, "Here it is, girls."

However it's done, the trickle of bees entering becomes a stream, then a river. And the job is over. If they light on the beekeeper's wife's prize syringa bush and she won't allow him to mutiliate it, then the bushel basket comes into play. He shakes the mass of bees down into the bushel basket, carries the whole business over to the hive and gently dumps the basket's contents on the ground in front of the alighting board. Mostly they'll run inside the hive. If they start in the other direction, the soft brush will sweep them back and turn them toward the hive entrance.

As I say, those are the easy problems. Suppose the bees pick a tree limb much too high to reach and much too thick to cut off. Then the ladder comes into play. The beekeeper will have to climb to get to them. If he can't get all of them into the basket one-handed without risking life and limb, perhaps he can set his hive on the stepladder top, and bring that up against the colony. Then he can knock a few at a time onto the alighting board and get them to set up that odor which calls the others.

Perhaps they're on a limb top too high for his stepladder

or on a limb too weak for his regular ladder. He may be able
to reach it and cut it off with his long limb cutter. Failing
that he uses his ball of string. He ties a rock to it, and either
himself throws it across the limb just back of the cluster, or
gets that little Dennis the Menace next door, who is probably
a pretty good baseball player, to do it for him.

He now has a strong string which has gone across the limb
and been brought back to earth by the stone. He takes the
two ends, holds them together, and jerks sharply. He keeps
jerking. Usually he can dislodge the bees, and usually when
they recluster they'll do so lower down. He may have to repeat this process a couple of times. But when he does get
them down where he can handle them, he can proceed as
above.

But the big test comes when the bees don't cluster right
there at home. The beekeeper has a transportation problem,
but he still doesn't want to lose his swarm.

So now he takes his bag and goes to the swarm by truck
or on foot, where it has clustered. If it is low down, he can
slip the bag over bees, branch, and the whole works, and
then cut the branch off. If that is impossible, he can brush
the bees into the bag. If it's too high to reach, he can attach
the mouth of the bag to the ring on his long pole, hold this
bag opening under the bees, and lift sharply to dislodge
them into it. Then he can tie the bag at the top and hang it
close by, and the remainder of the swarm will cluster on
the outside. He can carry the bag home and dump it out in
front of the empty hive by turning it inside out.

This colony we have just hived is called the "prime
swarm." In the natural state, or if the beekeeper is lax, or
conditions are unusual, a second swarm may very occasionally issue with one of the newly hatched queens. Even a third
may come after that. These are called "after-swarms," and in

most cases, unless the beekeeper is very clever, will deplete the original colony to the point where it will not survive. The after-swarms, too, will each be smaller than the one before and many times their queens may be unmated. They have little chance for survival. After-swarming should be avoided if humanly possible. Nothing but evil comes from it.

So this instinct of the bees to reproduce can be turned to the beekeeper's advantage, can be twisted to take it in directions he wants it to go. With good management (and an assist from a late honeyflow) it can mean capital wealth for him, and honey money jingling in his pocket. If stifling it is to his advantage, even this can be done to some extent by removing the causes. But the swarming instinct can never be stifled surely or completely.

And every little while a colony gets away to a hollow tree and freedom. Maybe the freedom is worth the price, but it seems doubtful. The bees don't gain much, except freedom from hive opening and manipulation on the part of the beekeeper and a chance to keep their surplus honey. They lose the fine hive, the medicine, the feeding with sugar water when their stores didn't last or during a poor honey year; they have, in other words, only a fraction of the chance they did have for survival.

Maybe they look back upon the old comforts with longing at first. Maybe they're just too busy to look back. More probably they don't think about these things at all.

6

---◆·◆---

HOLLOW TREE LIFE

Before man came along and began to control, manipulate and rob honeybees, they lived a great deal in hollow trees. They were and are, extremely smart about picking these homes. To begin with, they are almost never found in a dead hollow tree. If, occasionally, they are found in one, I believe that the tree died *after* the bees picked it, not before. So seldom are bees found in a dead tree that I am convinced they swarm out and abscond to a new home soon after a tree dies in which they are in residence.

But even in the finest of hollow trees, a fantastic number of bee-hours must go into cleaning it and preparing it for the storage of honey and pollen.

To do this a third substance in addition to honey and pollen is needed, which the bees must gather just the way they gather the other two. It is called "propolis." It is a substance about which the average person knows nothing. He probably has never even heard of it.

Propolis is not necessary to apiary life; in fact it is the bane of a beekeeper's existence. But it is completely essential to a honeybee colony's life in a hollow tree. The bees simply could not ready a hollow tree, live in it, protect it, store in it, without this little understood substance, propolis. And since it is so essential to hollow tree life, this is the place to examine its qualities at considerable length.

It is a gluelike material which the bees use for sticking things together, or giving them a smooth surface, or for filling cracks, or for performing any of dozens of other tasks.

Here again our tiny insect has certainly equaled, possibly outdone, the world's finest chemists. Because none of the great chemists or chemical organizations have produced any better glue for a bee's purposes than propolis, and I've never happened to run across one even as good. Furthermore the bees developed it countless centuries ago, long before Allied Chemical or DuPont, or for that matter even the United States itself, were even a gleam in an Indian's eye.

Propolis is a dark brown substance made primarily of the resinlike material from the buds of trees and plants. The bees collect it in their pollen baskets and carry it back to the hive. They collect it as needed, but for the most part, except in an emergency, this is not during the main honeyflow. Most of the heavy gluing of cracks and filling of holes comes in readying a hollow tree in the spring. In the fall, too, it is used in preparing for winter much the way a householder weather-strips and storm-windows his house when temperatures begin to drop.

It is usually in the fall of the year, too, that mice, on the lookout for winter quarters, will invade a tree and perhaps be stung to death. As we will explain more fully in the pages about the enemies of bees, the mouse body, which is too large to be carried outside by the bees, will be encased in propolis so that odor and decay will not affect either the inmates or the honey stores.

But don't get the idea that even at the height of the honeyflow the bees use propolis sparingly when they feel it is really needed. Take a hive tool and make a deep scratch on the inside wall of a beehive. Next time you open the hive, the scratch will be filled, the place smooth as a waxed tabletop. Furthermore the cover of the hive, which you removed to make the scratch, will be cemented back down again. If you took out any of the honey frames or brood frames so that you could have more room to wield the hive tool and make your scratch, the ends of those will be cemented in place again when next you open and inspect your hive.

But it is in the hollow-tree home that propolis really comes into its own. When the bees decide on a hollow-tree home, they remove from it every movable thing that they can carry. They lug out particles of rotten wood, the sawdustlike material left by borers, foreign matter of any kind.

Some years ago I cut a hollow tree for firewood that had once been a bee tree, but in which the colony had failed to winter. When I split the log, the inside was smooth and shiny, like an old polished antique. Anything the bees hadn't been able to remove they had covered over with propolis.

The whole inside had, after cleaning, been varnished with propolis, laboriously. I couldn't help thinking of the bee-hours that had gone into making the inside of that old hollow hickory as clean and smooth as the wood paneling over your fireplace. In one spot there was a V-shaped rotten place. They had cleaned all the rot from it and lacquered it until it was a deep beautiful V in the wood. All vestiges of rot were now removed or covered and the place looked, except for its shape which had been too wide to level off, just like the rest of the inside. It seemed almost a shame to burn anything so clean and so beautiful.

How do bees gather the resins if they are so very sticky, and carry them back to the tree or hive? Well, it isn't easy.

The bee pulls chunks of the stuff loose with her mandibles, and it will usually, being so sticky, string out. She will ball the string up with her second pair of legs and when the ball suits her, will place it in the pollen baskets much as she does when she gathers pollen. She'll sometimes take a little flight, then come back to add more to her load.

When she returns to the tree or hive, though, matters become very interesting, and mildly incredible. She can't get rid of her sticky load without help from one or more of her sisters. They come to her assistance. With their mandibles, the hive bees begin the unloading very much as the carrier pulled loose the pieces originally when she loaded herself. And this is hard work, backbreaking work. Transferring a load of nectar is nothing by comparison.

The hive bees brace themselves, bury their mandibles in the load. The carrier bee braces herself. Often her helpers pull so hard that she's dislodged from her hold. A novice in colony customs could be pardoned for thinking that these bees were fighting, or at the very least were having a tug of war over some choice morsel. Not so! This is another part of the communal effort among the bees with nobody apparently in charge, but the necessary work getting done.

Ordinarily the gathering of propolis starts no earlier than ten in the morning, and ends shortly after midafternoon. Probably this is because of the hardening proclivities of propolis. The bees need sun or warmth to be able to tear a load loose from the vegetation where it grew.

Occasionally a bee will get caught by colder weather in the late afternoon, and her sisters will be unable to relieve her of some of her load. This usually takes the shape of a stick-like projection. Such bees have been marked by scientists in an observation hive, and they did not go to the field the next morning. Instead they moved out onto the landing platform

Queen *(center)* about to back into cell to lay an egg.

Queen in act of laying, the back of her body deep in the cell, only her face showing in the direct center of the picture. Note many workers facing in toward her.

The daughters of Charles Mraz seem thrilled as he points out the queen to them. And they appear completely unafraid.

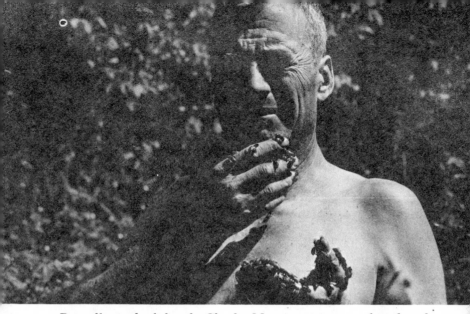

Bees all over both hands, Charles Mraz attempts to make a beard of them on his chin. *Below:* Charles, bare to waist, opens hive. The bee veil and gloves are on the author who is strictly leaving the bare torso to Charles.

Opening the hive.

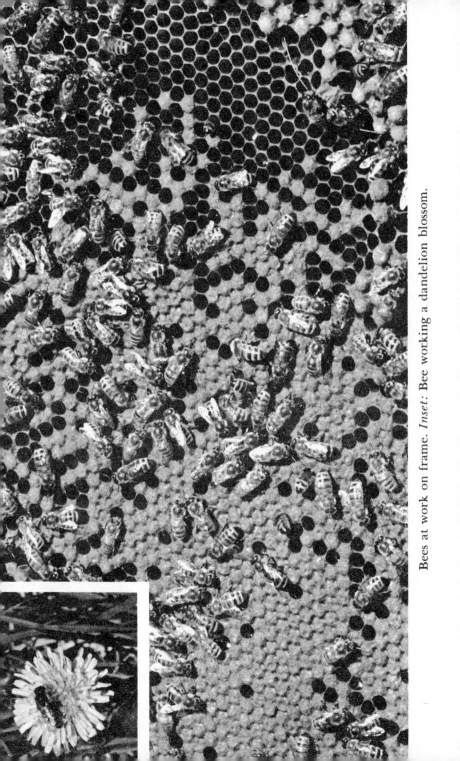

Bees at work on frame. *Inset:* Bee working a dandelion blossom.

Bees humped up fanning their wings to carry scent to others, communicating that hive is back together and work can go on again.

Mr. Carl Johnson, St. Albans, Vermont, uncapping with an electrically heated uncapping knife.

Mr. Johnson placing uncapped frame in extractor. (Empty supers in the background.)

Bees light on electrically charged wires, are shocked into stinging the pad underneath, from which their venom is collected for sale. *Below:* About $400 worth of dried bee venom.

(All photographs courtesy of Benjamin E. Rogers, Rogers Photo Service)

in the sun. By noon the appendages had become removable, and once free of them, these bees went back out into the field.

The hive bees carry the propolis with their mandibles to whatever spot in the tree or hive shows a need for it. It is spread with the mandibles, never with the tongue as was originally supposed.

The word "propolis" comes from two Greek words, "pro" and "polis." These words mean "before" and "city." The name stems from the custom of Caucasian bees, when in a wild state in a hollow tree with an opening that they consider to be too big to defend, of building small pillars of propolis lengthwise in front of the opening. These pillars are so engineered and so placed that there will be only one bee-width between any two of them. Thus, "before the city." A defense system setup in front of their small metropolis.

Propolis is a substance exactly right for their building and repair work, and certainly, up until recently at least, the envy of our whole adhesives industry.

Thus we see that the bees, after cleaning their new hollow-tree home, varnish the interior with propolis. They fill all cracks. They cover all signs of former occupancy with the same substance. They even cover the former occupant himself if he, understandably, has refused to give up his former home, has resented the intruders and fought it out. It is the basis for all tree life.

While this is going on, other bees commence the manufacture of wax from the honey they have brought with them to the tree in their honey stomachs. From the wax they build combs. These they need very soon and very badly. Without them there would be no place to store anything, no place for the queen to begin her laying of eggs.

These combs do not resemble the neat rectangular combs

that we shall later find are the rule in a hive. They are designed to fit the inside of the tree. They are, therefore, in most cases very long, and they are quite narrow in comparison with their width. I've seen them six feet long. There is no set shape, just as there is no set shape for a hollow tree.

These combs must be anchored firmly at the top and along the sides because of the weight of honey they must support. And since the space is irregular and there is no starter sheet, there will be a whole lot of extra and odd-sized cells along the sides when the space doesn't divide exactly into worker cell widths as it will in a manufactured frame. These larger cells may be used for honey storage, or they may, if they are in the brood chamber area, be used by the queen to raise drone bees. If there is a small irregularity in the inside shape of the tree trunk, this will be ingeniously brought into the comb pattern by the workers.

Because bees seem to like everything neat and symmetrical, they are likely to make all cells in a comb the same size. Thus if, without the beekeeper's starter, they begin making the larger cells in a comb or area, they are likely, in their passion for regularity, to make all the cells of that area the same size. There is, therefore, likely to be a great deal more large-celled comb in a bee tree than will be found in a hive.

No matter how many different-sized cells the bees may build, all those cells (except possibly the queen cells) will be hexagonal in shape. Scientists agree that no other shape would be as economical for bee purposes. Engineers with all their training, can come up with no better shape.

A series of squares would waste a tremendous amount of space when used for the rearing of round brood. A series of round cells that would fit the brood perfectly would waste space (in the form of small triangles) when piled one on top of the place where the two below touch. Round cells would waste material in extra wall space, too. Only the hexagonal shape comes close to the shape of the brood, has each wall fitting against the wall of another cell, and completely utilizes all space in the storage of honey.

The worker cell will be built exactly 4.83 cells to the inch. Even in a bee tree the majority of the cells will be this size. But in a hollow tree without starter, the engineering of the bees with no overall boss is incredible on all fronts. How can so many tiny minds gauge 4.83 cells to the inch so exactly? Even an engineer would need all sorts of instruments to measure. The bees have none.

They will start the top of the comb at several places. As this comb area approaches one of the others in being drawn out, the cells will be varied by the bees so gradually, the space divided by them so perfectly, that the change in size of each cell to prepare for the meeting is so infinitesimal it isn't in many cases discernible to the casual human eye.

Cut a piece of comb in the honeyflow and the bees will replace it with drone cells because these take less work and less wax. But they will be so ingenious about fitting the new comb in that only the "accommodation cells" where the new meets the old will be imperfect hexagons. There again your eye may pass over the imperfection, so neatly is it done by these amazing engineers.

Each comb area is started by one bee attaching her glob of wax at each spot from which the comb is to hang down. Other bees add their wax to it. And in doing so they begin to mold and thin the wax into walls for those tiny hexagons. They spread out the anchor area, begin more center stripping and more hexagonal cells out from each side of it.

It is completely incredible that, with thousands of bees coming up and adding their bit of wax to the spot where the "drawing out" is going on, you don't get a thousand different variations of shape and thickness. You're led to the conclusion that every one of these thousands of insects in her own right must be a trained engineer.

Each bee adds only a tiny part to a given area of comb. Yet each cell ends up the same size and shape as all the others. From the apparent disorganization and haphazard chaos of work on the combs comes the perfection of uniformity. When you see the work going on it even looks as if each bee constitutes herself an inspection party of one. She looks the work over, gives it a pat here and there and goes on about her business. With thousands of bees doing this, you somehow get that perfect finished product. Nobody knows who does the overall planning; actually there doesn't seem to be any, as we've pointed out. Everybody is boss. Yet the work gets done. That's the incredible part.

Each of our hollow-tree bees must use between seven and twenty pounds of honey to produce a pound of wax. Beekeepers don't agree at all on the amount, but do agree that it is considerable. And that a colony which already has drawn-out comb can store a vastly greater amount of honey.

When one bee adds her wax she will thin down the cell wall on which she decides to add it. Then she will leave the outer edge thick, just as she found it, for the next worker in her own turn to thin. The next bee will thin that edge and leave the new outer edge thick for her sisters to light on and use as a base for their work. Thin edges would not stand the crawling of the comparatively heavy bees. The thin cell wall without this thick edge would break down under bee weight. It is so thin that between two and three thousand thicknesses would be needed to measure one inch. And yet these tiny engineers know that wax this thin will hold their honey store perfectly. When they have capped it and finished it, it can be transported carefully clear across the United States or Europe without damage.

So our bees keep chewing up and softening those scales of wax which they take from their undersides, keep adding to the heavier center separator, and from it keep drawing out the thin-walled cells. There must be enough of those cells right away to accommodate the field bees returning with pollen and with nectar. And even more important, there must be enough of them to furnish bee-sized rooms in which the queen can begin to lay her eggs so that the colony can build up to strength again after the depletion of swarming. You can see that the amount of comb made is now of vital importance to the future safety, strength and security of the colony.

In a bee tree, the brood area is above, but close to, the opening. This is because the queen wants to start laying eggs as soon as possible, and the comb usually is anchored above and lengthened in a downward direction. The bees seem to prefer to store honey in the far reaches, preferring to crawl across the brood cells to get to the storage area rather than crawl across the stored honey to get to the brood. There is more tendency to intermingle brood and pollen and honey in a tree than in a hive. This may be to some extent because there is no beekeeper to requeen, and a queen past her prime has a tendency to produce a spotty brood nest with vacant cells in it.

There is another item which the bees may or may not have known enough to plan on. The hole in the tree lets in a lot of cold air; bees wintering above the opening will be warmer by a vital degree or two than they would be below the opening. Cold air from outside, if they were below, would

flow down across them like a waterfall. And in a hollow tree
there's no beekeeper to make the opening smaller, and place
it at the bottom with just that fact in mind.

So the combs progress downward and sideways, with bee
space between of just the right width, as if a human engineer
had planned it meticulously. Hundreds, thousands of bees
will dab at every bit of it, mold it, and change it. Again, remember that there is no master plan in a bee tree. Yet the
proper spacing, the proper size to the cells, comes out as if a
foreman stood over the workers with a set of blueprints.

But the need for so much wax to make so much comb,
takes its toll of the amount of honey the new wild colony
can store in preparation for winter. Nothing is made easy for
them the way it is in the hive by the beekeeper.

First off, as the brood begins to hatch, the wild colony will
produce a lot more drones than there is any need for, because
there will be more drone cells made than there would have
been in a regulated hive. Every drone produced by the new
colony is one worker less to function as a hive and later as a
field bee. Sometimes when a wild colony gets started and
makes whole areas of drone cells, they'll produce enough
drones so the safety of the colony will be jeopardized. There
should be no drones, once the hive has swarmed.

Then, the round opening is against them. If it is small
enough to keep out robber bees and squirrels and chipmunks
and birds, it is too small to handle efficiently the vast stream
of bees that comes with nectar during the honeyflow. If it is
big enough to handle its bees in honeyflow time, it is too
big to defend and will let in too much draft in winter. It's
better that it should be too small, though, than too large.

Further, if it's too small, the bees coming in must hover in
front of the opening waiting their chance to get in, because
there will be no alighting board. When the bees want to

ventilate it, in extremely hot weather, the lack of an alighting board is crucial. There's no place for them to stand and do their humped-up fanning act. Usually in a tree there's no winter ventilation opening (not counting the main opening), no way for the moisture to be carried off. And moisture can give the bees dysentery, can even freeze on them on a zero day and kill out the colony.

In fact, you wonder how bees in the wild state exist, and have existed for centuries, so mercilessly are the cards stacked against their survival. But they do and always have.

Always they must fight harder against marauders than they would have had to with a slit opening. The round hole is ideal for letting in rodents, birds and other enemies and is amazingly hard to defend.

One of the biggest drawbacks to hollow-tree life for a bee colony is space itself. If there's too much space the body warmth of the bees can't temper the air even a little bit. Still, that is much preferable to too little space. If there is too little space for storage, there won't be enough to eat come late winter, and the colony will die. Or even if there's enough space to winter them during a normal winter yet not enough to build up a good surplus, once a poor honey season comes along the colony will die out for lack of this surplus. A colony that swarmed from the same apiary on the same day and was hived, however, would be fed by the beekeeper and would come through such a crisis in fine shape.

One enemy against which the bees in a tree are helpless is the forest fire. If it threatens them, they will fill their honey stomachs upon smelling smoke, to be ready to fly somewhere else and start again. It's about the only chance they have for survival. A flash fire in undergrowth below them might not destroy their tree. But in their panic they would not know this. Waiting too long would be fatal because their wings are easily singed, causing them to drop into the path of the flames. Even if they do get away safely as a colony, the queen with them—and this is not assured because both queen and colony hate to leave—they may not all leave together.

Their best bet is to stay with the tree. Then if it is not actually burned, and their air fanning functions successfully, so great is the insulation power of wood that their combs may remain mostly intact and they may survive. If the fire should come during the August drought, their chances of surviving away from the tree would be nil anyhow. They couldn't draw out and fill new comb in a new tree and store enough honey to winter them.

But this is even beyond the power of the bees to realize. They only know it is a terrifying calamity, a disaster of gigantic proportions. They must make a decision, and whatever they decide will test their fortitude and staying power and collective ability to the utmost. No matter what happens, death, both for the individual and for the colony, holds all the cards.

Diseases as well as a colony's other enemies, are helped by the hollow tree setup. A wild German colony can get European Foul Brood and be unable to clean it out and survive. American Foul Brood will kill any colony, but in addition will probably infest every other colony, wild or in an apiary, within a couple of miles, because those colonies will in all probability rob the stores of the colony that died of infection. Thus they in turn will be infected.

Bears naturally live in woods, and if the shell of the bee tree is thin near the entrance, they will rip it open with claws and teeth until they can reach a paw in for globs of comb and honey and, most delicious, unhatched grubs. The colony will die because the bear will return. And even if he should not, the entrance is now too enlarged to protect the colony from weather, robbers and other marauders.

Kingbirds are offered a safe and handy perch on the tree limbs, from which they can fly out and catch one returning bee after another. To be sure, those same limbs do offer a cooling shade which the commercial hive won't have. The solid area above the hollow will offer insulation better than anything a hive roof can offer. But these are minor matters compared with the major drawbacks.

The majority of hollow trees—by no means all, but the majority—are to be found in woods. If the tree is any distance back from the edge of the woods, the bees have to fly across that completely unproductive area before they can get into farm and crop acreage. And they need clover or orchard areas where nectar can be found in quantity. Again if the woodland is extensive at all, a mile or two in width, bees at one edge must fly always in one direction for nectar. Bees from a commercial beeyard will be able to bring in stores from a 360-degree circle around them. But bees at the edge of a sizable woods have only 180 degrees for their foraging trips.

You must add to this, too, the fact that bees in picking a tree to live in don't seem to carry their selectivity to the matter of source of supply. If they would pick out a tree in a woods at the edge of an alfalfa field, or next to an apple orchard or an orange grove, life would be very good for them. But they don't seem to do this. That seems to be one place the brain of a bee falls down; they pick the home tree for other reasons, and then depend on their wings to get them to and from the source of supply. This is a far cry from the careful transporting of a colony to the middle of a huge honey supply likely to be done by a beekeeper with all *his* colonies.

Lastly the bees in a hollow tree have far more to fear from humans than the bees in an apiary, even taking into consideration the robbing, the manipulation, and the control of an apiary hive.

Men hunt bees; we'll talk about that at length in a chapter under that heading, and give you methods. When a hunter finds a bee tree, with few exceptions he must cut down the tree to get the stores. Most of the time the hunter is not a beeman and has no desire to try to save the colony. He just cuts the tree and lets the bees fend for themselves. The hunter usually "takes up" the tree after the honeyflow, so that even if the bees were able to keep their queen unharmed and were to find a new home in another tree, there wouldn't be time for honey storage. Except in warm-all-year climates, this would just postpone destruction of the colony.

Thus the beekeeper robs only the excess, takes the responsibility upon himself for the well-being of the colony when he owns it. But when a hunter finds a colony in the wild state, if he's to take any of the honey he must take it all. And the colony is left to die off, or, if the queen is killed, to join other colonies if any of them will tolerate additions and not kill the newcomers as robbers.

The very industry of the bees provides them with no defense against man. If they knew enough to abandon the hole in their hollow tree when they saw some man near it, possibly looking up into various trees, they could make their discovery almost insurmountably difficult. But bees know only that they have scarcely enough time before winter. They must work and work. There is no such thing in their makeup as delay. And so the man looking for them gets their entrance hole against the light. And there they are, entering and leaving constantly, the newcomers hovering a foot from the hole, waiting their chance to enter. And they have given themselves away. Working uninterruptedly is their undoing.

If they are deep in the woods, they find access to nectar more of a problem. And they are more in danger from bears. But if they are deep in the woods with trees close around them on all sides, they have a far better chance of remaining undiscovered by humans. Too, the farther up in the air their hollow is located the better chance they have of surviving hunting expeditions. The chances of a reasonably high-up colony being spotted by any but bee hunters is almost nil, because people walking in the woods almost never look up. If they do, they would be lucky to catch the tree hole against open sky, and without that there would be little chance the casual passerby would discover it.

There's one way in which, though, a wild colony can win in their effort to circumvent man without being deep in a woods. A number of colonies have stumbled upon the method. That is to pick a hollow in a shade tree right in the middle of a highly populated town or city. The colony will surely be discovered. But nobody can cut a shade tree, one owned by the city. And if the bees are high enough up so that they never annoy those on the sidewalks below, or rather those down below never annoy the bees enough to make them sting, then they have it made. They have a home protected by cops and city grounds-maintenance men. And with all those lawns with all that clover growing in them, the source of nectar supply is bountiful. There aren't even many bees near to compete for the nectar.

Such a colony remained for years in a big maple between the sidewalk and the street in front of the post office in Vergennes, Vermont. Everybody knew it was there. But the bees bothered nobody. Nobody was allowed to bother them. I saw them for many years each summer; they may still be there for all I know.

So, to sum up, it is natural for bees to seek a hollow tree for their living quarters, and this instinct, in our modern world, does not provide as safe a home for them as would a hive. There are more enemies, and there is no one to protect them. Too, there is no one to take over if they are unable to fend for themselves for any reason. They are likely to lose everything, instead of just the surplus honey. And loss of surplus honey doesn't much matter as regards their survival when the game is played according to beekeeper's rules.

Hollow tree life is freedom, complete. But it is a freedom gained at the expense of security. In human circles the giving up of security for freedom makes sense. Through the centuries the chance to do so has been grasped by country after country without a backward glance.

In the case of the bees, it is my feeling that the price paid far outweighs the gain.

7

HIVE LIFE

As we have seen, since the first written history of the human race, man has been robbing the bees of their stores. The bees weren't happy about this, but they were outmaneuvered.

At first the robbery was brutal and destroyed the colony. The hollow tree had to be cut down to get at the honey, and the man who committed the robbery, in those early days before bee veils, seldom got away unscathed.

Then subtlety began to rear its head. The first actual out-maneuvering was to build cyclinders, closed at one end, and also closed but with some system of entrance holes at the other end. These cylinders were placed where they would attract swarming bees. Often they were smeared with some-thing sweet which would more swiftly get the bees to come there. Once they came there they were theoretically im-pressed by the accommodations, and when their colony swarmed they would, as scouts, recommend this location.

These cylinders were made out of bark, or were fashioned from the hollow trunk of a tree, or were put together from some other material. In Egypt for centuries they were made from the mud of the river Nile, much like pottery.

When the bees had filled the cylinder with honey, the bee-keeper got rid of the bees, often by building a fire under them, took out the honey and the wax for his use, and stored the hive somewhere for next season. This was easier than cutting down a bee tree, but was just as rough on the bees.

The next step was to make for the bees a hive of braided straw called a "skep." This had a round hole through which the bees could come and go. The hive was fairly wide at the base and was rounded-in on all sides to a point on top. It was shaped a little like a bell, or a Seckel pear.

When this straw hive was full of honey, the beekeeper killed the bees with fumes of some sort, mainly sulphur fumes, ripped apart the straw and had the honey. Still it was tough on the bees.

All these robbery methods left a lot to be desired. Cutting the tree would give you a mixture of broken comb, dead bees, brood, bee bread, wax and honey if the hollow was any distance up in the tree so that it would land hard when the tree came down. Perhaps there'd be pieces of rotten wood to give it flavor. The whole thing had to be strained through cloth to be worth anything to anybody. And it had a pretty rank, wild taste as a result.

The cylinder and skep methods were nearly as bad as the tree cutting. Everything wasn't so thoroughly broken up, but the same ingredients were present, and if you tried to eat the honey as comb, instead of straining it, you were likely to bite into a just-maturing bee (complete with stinger), or a cell full of bee bread, or even a few cells of larvae. It would be hard to determine which of the three would be the worst. In my experience bee bread tastes like sawdust when a very poor grade of wood has been used.

In all cases the colony was done for. You'd have to leave

some of your hives over the winter to swarm the next spring, or you'd very soon run out of colonies.

To avoid this bee destruction, way back before the Christian era, beekeepers began to insert bars in the skeps from which the bees could hang their combs. A few of these could be cut out and removed, and new bars inserted in their places. This would give the beekeeper honey and still allow a colony a chance to survive and be robbed again next season. With this setup Aristotle, in 342 B.C., even practiced colony dividing. In the spring he'd cut out some of the bars that had brood comb, and put them in another skep. He knew by then that the queenless hive would produce a new queen from among the larvae.

There also were wicker skeps or hives, and these were cloomed. This meant that they were banked with a mixture of dirt and cow manure to protect them from the weather and the cold. They had a straw roof on top. The idea of eating honey from a cloomed hive would pretty thoroughly alienate the modern housewife if she knew about it, and she very well might know.

Beekeepers, in areas where lumber was plentiful, began to build square boxes for bees. Later, like the skeps, bars were inserted from which the combs were to be hung.

After that, man became even smarter. He began to try to design and build homes for his bees that would allow him to rob them without damaging any comb, brood, eggs, larvae, bee bread; that would even leave a minimum supply of honey stored for the bees for winter.

The perfect hive should, he knew, do two things; it should provide a good home for the bees, and it should be easy for the beekeeper to open, examine, manipulate, and rob. The old hollows and the cylinders and the skeps had provided the first. But he needed a new conception of a hive, possibly with removable frames and addable storage areas that could be put on after the brood area was complete and would thus hold only pure honey. He had working for him the bees' instinct for raising young and carrying on the chores of the hive as near the opening as possible while they stored the honey in the far reaches of the available space. They didn't like to crawl over good honey to reach the work area, and marauder bees from other colonies found it increasingly hard to steal successfully the farther in from the entrance they had to go to find the stored honey.

The patents on record in the U. S. Patent Bureau tell a tale of the present hive's evolution. Beemen who knew all about bees, inventors who knew nothing about bees, and farmers all worked out ideas. There were drawers that the bees could fill with comb and honey, which you'd pull out the way you'd pull out a bureau drawer when you went after a clean pair of socks. This didn't work because of propolis. The bees glued in those drawers so completely that the inventor had to splinter them and break the comb to get them out.

There was the Stewarton shallow-bar hive with glass strips between the bars, back in 1819. There were hives where you opened the sides instead of the top. There were hives with boxes which provided more storage space at the sides. There were octagonal hives, square hives, rectangular hives, round hives. There was the first glass observation hive, and there were multiple hives which were like bee apartment houses. Huber even invented a leaf hive which opened like the pages of a book. Here again the bees and their propolis were non-cooperative.

Finally over the years, matters pretty well boiled down to the almost square, fairly shallow, wooden hive of the present day. This was a box open at the top and bottom. If you took off the roof, similar wooden boxes could be fitted on to increase the available space as more storage area was needed by the bees.

On the inside there were removable frames that would hang down and would fill the opening in the box. The bees would fill the lowest box with brood and a little honey. It would be nearest the entrance. When it was almost full the beekeeper would fit another box atop the first one. And after that was almost full he would add a third atop the second. These extras the beekeeper called "supers." Each box would fit atop any other interchangeably, and the roof would fit on top of them all.

At the end of the season, theoretically, the beekeeper could remove all the boxes on top of the bottom box and have pure honey for himself. The bees, their queen, their brood and some supplies, were safe in the bottom box. They were relatively undisturbed by the removal of the top boxes, and would be able to produce a lot more honey for the beekeeper again the next season. This, briefly and in a general way, was the idea behind the new hive that evolved over many decades.

But once the basic idea and the shape were accepted, the argument about size began. Some argued for a deep hive box that would be completely square, some said this greater depth would cause the combs to sag from the greater weight. Some argued for a hive that would be an exact cube; it would conserve the body heat of the bees best, since the bees cluster in a ball in winter, and broodnests are usually a sphere. But a small cube hive, when enough cube-shaped supers were added on top, would blow over. And a large cube would have units too heavy to handle, especially by the elderly, or by women beekeepers. There were hive boxes of different sizes called the Gallup, the Heddon, the Danzen-baker, the Jumbo, the American, the Quinby, the Adair, the Dadant. And the Langstroth.

The Langstroth was the one that outlasted all but a couple of the others and is today used by some 95 percent of the United States beekeeping industry. This was a comparatively shallow-framed hive with frames 17⅝ inches long and 9⅛ inches deep. The frames have a heavy top piece, and the ends of this top piece stick out so that it will hang from a cleat or a rabbeted groove in opposite walls inside. Nowadays the frames are self-spacing. Those frame ends that stick out are enough wider than the rest of the frame top so that, when they are touching, the remainder of the frames and the combs that the bees build inside them, will be exactly the right distance apart to provide optimum working space for the house bees and the queen. Exactly ten frames can be hung in the hive.

Rev. L. L. Langstroth, a Presbyterian minister, was the inventor of this hive, and more particularly of the frames that fitted into it. Throughout the history of beekeeping, ministers have added greatly to the knowledge of beekeeping equipment, and of bees. Dzierzon, too, was a minister. Evidently the weekday leisure allowed by the workload of the ministry, fitted nicely with the owning of a few swarms of bees.

Briefly, the advantages responsible for the long-term victory of the Langstroth hive and frame are these: it is low and flat enough to allow other hive units to be added if needed until it can be higher than a man without blowing over. This is why, when you pass an apiary in midsummer, you sometimes see some hives as much as six or seven feet tall, while others are only a couple of feet tall. You can tell the strong swarms at a glance.

In addition, the shallow comb is easier to uncap when the honey is to be extracted, because the uncapping knife is long enough to take off all the caps with only one stroke. The shallow comb is also less likely to kill bees when lifted out than a deeper one would be. And, most important of all, in a Langstroth hive, when the bees cluster for winter just above the opening and begin to eat their stores, the cluster will work up and reach the top of the hive where conditions should be the warmest when the weather is really cold. It will eat its way across the top during the very coldest months. By the time the bees start down the far side, the weather should have moderated a little.

So nowadays, the hive which most beemen in the United States use in their apiaries has a hive stand, the front of which slopes down for an alighting board, and which gets the hive up off the ground.

On top of this there fits a bottom board. Set in the front of it is an ingenious device that lies across the width of the hive and which, with different sides turned out, will give you different-sized openings into the hive for the bees in line with colony needs of the moment.

Next comes the hive body or brood chamber, open at the top and bottom, and with frames. Then above that, identical hive bodies with frames which are still called supers, and which will afford extra space for honey storage. There can be many or few of these, as we have mentioned. Above that is the inner cover, and above that the hive cover or roof, which fits down over the inner cover and the top of the top super. And there is your hive.

Naturally this was, all the way through, thievery, unfair; you're going to condemn the beekeepers for fixing things so they could shamelessly work these insects and rob them. Anybody with any feeling for the underdog would think this way.

Actually you don't need to feel sorry for the bees. The hive has worked out just as well for the bees as it has for the bee-keepers. All the bees ever wanted from their labor was enough honey to insure them plenty to eat in lean times and in winter. And a warm, dry home, safe from marauders.

The beekeeper removes the surplus honey, yes. But in doing so he also guarantees the bees plenty to eat. As we saw in the previous chapter, if there is a lean year, a long winter, trouble of any kind, the beekeeper feeds his little colony of workers on sugar and water or honey until the flowers are in bloom again, while the wild colony dies. That's all that any extra store of honey could do anyway.

In addition, the beekeeper protects his bees from all the hollow tree problems we examined. He shoots black bears, he lays poison around the area to kill mice and skunks, he manipulates the hive if it should grow weak, possibly combining it with another weak hive so that neither dies out. He gives extra insulation in winter where needed, and roof insulation or shade in summer to protect the hive from the sun.

Furthermore, the home which the beekeeper furnishes is palatial—a mansion—compared with that old hollow tree. Let's look at some of the refinements that he has installed to solve problems that for centuries had troubled the world of bees.

First there was always that problem of cleaning out the inside of a hollow tree. The beekeeper's hive was already clean.

Then there was the matter of the opening's size. The bee-keeper furnishes a slit for an entrance, perfect from a bee's point of view, nearly mouse and squirrel proof. In addition, that ingenious block of wood in the opening can be changed to make different-sized openings depending on the strength and needs of the colony.

In her wild existence, the bee hung her combs at the top and drew them out to incredible lengths, curved some of them to fit curved contours. These narrow combs were very long.

But the hive combs, built in the frames, are nowhere near as long or heavy and so don't need such heavy wax construction. The frame is completely removable.

Since the size and construction of the frames is standard on all but a few hives, they are completely interchangeable, too. A beekeeper can lift out a frame, examine it, return it to its place, or replace it with a different frame. He can even move it to another hive. He can destroy drone or queen cells built in the corners, learn how well everything is going in the hive. Inspection tells him when he has diseased brood or when he should add more room via another super.

In trees or skeps all the comb had to be built up. But when the bee enters the super which the beekeeper has provided, matters are very different. If it's the large, standard-size super, not only are the frames in there, but most of the time each frame is complete with cells all drawn out and waiting to be filled with honey. The bees—and they must be practically purring with delight at this break—fly out into the fields at once, instead of spending hours and using up a lot of precious honey making the necessary wax to build those cells.

The reason the cells are all complete and ready for filling is that the beekeeper found a way to remove the honey from cells by only damaging them to the extent of uncapping them. This was the extracting process we've mentioned. He'd uncap the honey-filled cells in the frames he had removed, and put them in a machine called an extractor. The machine would then whirl the frames very rapidly so that the honey would be forced out of the cells by centrifugal force against the inside walls of the machine. It would then flow down to the bottom and could be drawn off through a valve.

When the honey had all been whirled out, the frames could be removed from the machine, fitted into a super, and be ready for refilling. No bee-time is consumed in making new cells, no excess honey eaten in bee-manufacture of wax. Probably—though it's admittedly risky to presume to think like a bee—the workers would rather be out in the world of sunshine and flowers than hanging in a dark hive, waiting for wax to form, and building with it. The result: beekeeper, honey eater, bees, all happy. The honey is clear golden in color, where the strained honey was never that pure or beautiful.

After a while the white wax, where it is crawled over numberless times by numberless thousands of bees, grows darker and darker with "travel stain" until it is a dark, dark brown. This seems incongruous in an insect that walks on nothing dirtier than flower petals and white honeycomb.

But do you remember that pad with hairs between the claws of the bee's foot? When the claws start to slip it presses on this pad and makes a sticky fluid come from the base of the hairs. The bee doesn't slip any more, but the fluid causes the travel stain on the comb. The result is that when you see a beekeeper putting back used comb, it is sometimes almost black. You wonder if it is artificial, or colored in some way. Not so; it just marks the passage of millions of bee feet. When these cells are filled and capped, the new white cap is in striking contrast to the color of the cells.

Beekeepers came up with another smart idea to avoid comb that got started as drone cells for some reason. They made beeswax into a flat sheet and then stamped on it the exact hexagons that the bees consider standard for worker-cell shape and size. This sheet of stamped beeswax is called "starter." It's there—it's easy. The bees just draw it out. It's attached to the middle of the top of the frame in place of the heavy wax partition with which bees divide the comb in half to make cells on each side. This dividing promotes strength and easy filling from both sides. No bee seems to be giving orders to divide each comb lengthwise, but it's always done that way.

The bees then draw out the stamped design on each side, and there are the cells. The cells are all standard worker. And even here where combs must be drawn out, not as much beeswax is needed from the colony as is needed to make comb without starter. The cells are even slanted up a little so that the product surely won't spill out before the cap is begun.

Some beekeepers put in only a small amount of starter, just a rectangle or a triangle, and let the bees take it from there. But more feel that they're ahead financially if the bees spend the extra time out in the fields, and they furnish starter enough to make the whole, or almost the whole, partition. Fine wires are used in the large frames for strength. They are embedded in the starter with heat. The wires keep the comb from sagging so that it can be filled, extracted, and used again and again and again. Thus, using starter, the beekeeper cuts way down on drone cells, makes for a little more honey and economy all around.

Some supers are half the size of standard supers. These are for the production of pound boxes of comb honey. Before the machine to extract honey was perfected, a tremendous amount of comb honey in pound boxes was sold. The strained honey wasn't as appetizing-looking as the extracted honey is, and there was no saving of money because the wax cells were just as definitely destroyed in the straining as if they had been eaten. The beekeeper's costs weren't cut by using the cells again and again. And he couldn't pass on the saving in lower prices.

Many people these days have never seen comb honey in pound boxes. One city woman, when we served small chunks of comb honey with hot biscuits, asked if it was Vermont maple syrup. But in the earlier days of beekeeping, everybody knew comb honey; it was all they did know. They didn't, however, understand the method for getting it into those square wooden frames. If you told people the bees put it there, not the beekeeper, you'd get a look of utter skepticism.

But that was exactly how it was done—and still is for that matter—wherever pound boxes of comb honey are still sold. The pound boxes are about half as high as standard combs, and that is the reason those supers are roughly half as tall as regular supers.

Instead of hanging frames inside these smaller supers, the beekeeper fills his super with square wooden pound boxes. In each of these boxes he attaches a cut sheet of starter, the way he would in a frame. He usually puts in 28 of these boxes.

The bees draw out the starter, fill the boxes. The beekeeper removes them, scrapes off the propolis with which the bees cemented them together, places each in a cardboard carton with his name and advertising on it, and sends them off to market. The smaller supers, with half-height frames to fit, are also sometimes used for extracting.

When you're not accustomed to eating comb honey, you find yourself chewing until you've pretty well swallowed all the honey and still have a glob of wax in your mouth. You just have to get the knack of swallowing wax and honey together. If you concentrate a little on it at first, it pretty soon becomes automatic. To some of us, even those of us who use extracted honey most of the time, comb honey now and then (maybe with those warm biscuits I mentioned), is a treat.

Two other inventions which have made the beekeeper better able to service his colonies without hurting bees or letting them kill themselves stinging him, and without upsetting them unduly, are the bee veil and the smoker. The bee veil is just what its name implies, a hat with a wire screening hanging down from the brim, and below that, a baggy pull-over-type shirt with a drawstring in the bottom. The bees can't sting through the heavy canvas of the hat, and they can't reach you through the screen. With heavy trousers and heavy gloves, you're pretty safe at work. Though I hasten to add that many, many beekeepers don't use a bee veil or any other protection. And Charlie Mraz, New England's largest beekeeper, in summer works among his beehives stripped to the waist. There might be the smell of fear on non-beekeepers who tried the same thing; probably such a person would be stung.

Some have said that the bees just "get to know" their owner. In a bee article which I once wrote for the *Saturday Evening Post,* the only illustration was of Charlie, bare to the waist, covered with bees in a buzzing vest. Bees were hanging down from his chin like a beard. I happen to know that this picture was taken down South in someone else's beeyard, since our area was under snow at the time. Which would pretty well explode the thought that the bees don't sting a beekeeper because they know him.

The smoker is a hand-sized bellows and firebox. Punky material, or green or wet material, is lighted inside the firebox. Then when the bellows part is squeezed, smoke shoots out of the opening. Directed into a hive, this has an instantaneously quieting effect. The bee's instinct tells her that fire threatens her home.

She goes at once about filling her honey stomach from the combs, as we would expect. Too, the smoke may have a deadening effect on a bee's respiratory system. Or there may be some other reason no one has yet discovered for the quieting, for the departure of belligerence, and for the filling with honey.

But whatever the reason, the effect is just what the beekeeper wants it to be. The smoker has taken the dread out of handling those occasional ugly swarms.

The hive tool, which pries, scrapes and does all sorts of other useful tasks, has been a great boon to both bee and beekeeper, too. And the bee escape has made hive manipulation easier and less costly, the honey house windows more nearly free from imprisoned bees. A queen excluder which allows the smaller workers to pass through but not the queen, helps keep brood out of the supers and helps run the colony to the advantage of all, without needless loss of insect life.

The bee escape is an ingenious device; it looks like a piece of plywood exactly the size of a super. In the center of it there is a metal hole designed to let a bee pass through from one direction, but preventing her from passing through in the opposite direction.

The beekeeper pries up with his hive tool on the super or supers he wishes to remove from the main part of the hive. These are literally full of bees, working, storing. To carry the whole business to the honey house would be a frightful disturbance, even waste, of bees.

He removes the supers, places the plywood bee escape atop the main part of the hive, and then replaces the supers atop the bee escape. He leaves it there for a while. When he returns the bees have all crawled down through the bee escape into the main hive as they finished their work, and no bees have been able to crawl back up in there from the hive below. The result? One or more supers clean of bees to remove for good. Big beekeepers who work outyards and can't wait, also use a chemical placed at the top of the hive, the fumes of which drive the bees down and out. This cleans the supers in minutes.

In hive life, just as in tree life, the work goes on while every worker is apparently on her own with no chain of command. By some instinct the new bee knows what nurse work needs doing, pitches in and does it. Somehow there are enough others doing the nurse work *they* find to do, so that it all gets done.

The same is true of the rest of the housework; the cleaning of cells, the preparing them for egg laying, the manufacturing of wax, the building of comb, the guard duty, the fanning for circulation. In all these jobs in hive life that incredible lack of command crops up. There may be such command, but man has as yet been unable to prove it or even to sight it.

For instance, if comb is needed fast, workers appear in quantity at the scene to make it. When the job is pretty well along, workers desert the comb-making chore at that particular place. Just enough remain to carry the chore on at the rate needed. The easy and obvious explanation is that workers see a need, jump to the doing of it. Other workers join in. After a little a new worker, coming upon that scene, sees the need but sees enough of her sisters working on the problem. She goes on to something else. This idea presupposes the power to reason on the part of a tiny insect. But how else can you look upon it?

Another example is the task of ventilation. The bees hump

themselves up and move their wings about 400 times a second on the landing area of the hive on a hot day. You can't see the wings; all you see is a group of humped up wingless bees standing rigid. They are setting up a circulation which provides their working sisters with the air they need, and takes up the moisture from the curing of the honey in the uncapped cells.

The hotter it gets inside, or the more moisture-laden the air becomes, the greater the number of bees that will stand there fanning. Who tells them they must? Nobody as far as anyone can ascertain. They decide it needs doing and go about doing it. The more it needs doing, the more bees do it. They see a great need as they pass by, stop and pitch in.

The same is true of guard duty. Which ones are selected for this duty? Who selects them? Again, nobody knows. If guards are having trouble with ants or small animals, or if there is heavy robbing by other bees from other hives, there will be extra guards. They've sensed danger and rallied around. When the danger lessens, some will go to other things.

In the matter of ventilation in their hive life, there is more than just the beating of wings. The bees have figured out the world's first air-conditioning system. Furthermore, believe it or not, they did it long before man was able to do it. Just as in the matter of the perfect shape for a cell, where there were problems which only a highly trained engineer or a completely untrained bee could solve, so in air conditioning the untrained bee beat the highly trained engineer to the solution.

When the weather gets very, very hot and the sun of summer beats down on the roof of the hive, the temperature inside that hive may shoot up in spite of plain bee fanning. Think how hot the inside air in your car would become if you left it all afternoon in the hot sun with one of the windows down only a tiny slit.

Honeycomb softens at about 115 degrees Fahrenheit. The whole life of the hive depends on keeping that comb intact. If it should melt, the eggs would sink to the bottom of the hive; the larvae, the pupae, would become uncovered and would not have food. The bee bread would join the rest of the mess in the bottom of the hive, and atop it all would drop down the winter's stores of liquid food. The loss of brood, or food, or storage space, would each in itself be enough to cause the colony to perish.

As you can see, then, it is absolutely essential that the temperature be kept down. The bees, if it becomes necessary when plain fanning is not doing the job, lay aside other tasks.

They go out, find water, and bring it back in their honey stomachs in place of nectar. Hundreds of them, even thousands of them carry it. They spread it on the combs, on the inside walls of the hive. The fanners, augmented in number, have taken their places. They still circulate the air in that humped up stance of theirs. The evaporation of the water the others have brought in (and of the water that is in the nectar and must be evaporated in the curing process) cools the inside of the hive. It provides a crude but very effective air-conditioning.

It is so effective, in fact, that the hive air, instead of being much hotter than the outside air as you would expect, is often even cooler. Who taught the bees this engineering principle? Who tells them when to start putting it into practice? No one knows.

But certainly they do it. A friend of mine a short time ago told a group I was standing with at a party that bees must get very thirsty in hot weather.

"Thousands of them come to my bird bath and drink up all the water. I have to keep refilling it over and over."

I explained to the lady that this was not so; that the bees were taking this water home for their air conditioning. But I doubt if she believed me. My explanation was so absurd that I should hardly have expected anyone who could see with her own eyes that the bees were thirsty and were drinking, to believe me.

Other people have seen bees along the edges of ponds, streams, puddles—any water, the nearer their home the better. And they've marveled at it. I'm sure the true explanation is far more to marvel at than anything they thought of.

There are stories of fires that burned farm buildings. In one such case the heat was fantastic; so great that the beehive nearby burst into flame.

A fireman hit it with a hose spray and put it out. When the excitement died down it was found that all the bees had rallied around during the fire and worked on the air-conditioning. The bees from the field, coming home, had seen the need and started helping. Many, many bees fanned furiously throughout the fire at the door on the side away from the flames. Thousands carried water.

And when the hive top was lifted off, everything was intact inside. The outside wall was scorched and burned, but with an assist from the one fireman who had seen the hive start burning, the bees had saved their wax structure, their stores, and their colony life. Some may have filled themselves with honey to be ready to leave. But once they saw they had a chance to survive, all must have gone back to work.

Thus the hive life is a very ordered thing. The colony lives in neatness and order. No animal or insect except man, keeps his quarters more scrupulously clean.

The young bees work first in the hive at housekeeping

tasks. Then they take to the field, and from then on bring nectar and pollen to the colony. We have seen that they literally work themselves to death at the height of a honeyflow.

There are many, many tasks. The bees pitch in and do whatever seems to need doing, in direct ratio to the urgency of the need. There is in their home life, as far as any observer has been able to tell, no loafing, no bickering about tasks, no selfishness. Each contributes selflessly, to the fullest extent of her capabilites, for the good of the entire colony, throughout her short life.

Through engineering know-how their life pattern is highly efficient. They understand the curing of a product which sours without their ministrations. But even these wonders are transcended by their ability to communicate one with another, which we will examine in the next chapter.

8

---◆·◆---

COMMUNICATION

Bees can't talk as we talk; we all know that. But don't for a moment get the idea they can't communicate with one another in running their complex communal establishment. A honeybee can actually direct another honeybee to a source of nectar as surely and as accurately as you can direct a friend to a bargain at one of the stores downtown.

She can communicate to the other bee the exact direction to travel, how far in that direction to go, and how exciting a source of supply she'll find when she gets there.

Now this sounds incredible on the face of it. I realize that. It doesn't make sense that a little insect only about half an inch long, has a brain big enough to work out a communication system that can do with great accuracy the things I've mentioned above.

But that's how it is. The whole thing then enters the realm of the fantastic when you learn that the instructions are given on a vertical surface in the dark. They must later be translated into a horizontal flight line by the receiving bee.

The perpendicular line of gravity is used by the bees to

represent the direction of the sun from the hive. The bee that has found the source of supply shows the angle from the vertical. Thus she shows other bees the angle of horizontal flight in relation to the position of the sun.

If that sounds complicated, it's because it is. And these tiny insects worked it out through the generations from sheer necessity. I'd seriously doubt if humans could come up with a better system, if they had no voice, no arms to point with, and had to do it in the pitch dark cramped in between library stacks full of honey.

From the very first of man's relationship with bees, he found that if one honeybee discovered a very promising source of food and returned full to her hollow tree or hive, shortly a lot of bees would appear where the first one had found the gathering so lucrative. Beekeepers said that the first bee had "brought" others with her.

As beekeeping increased in importance, beekeepers began to notice a peculiar "dance" which returning bees sometimes performed on the comb. It was done in a small circle, and other nearby bees seemed to grow excited when they watched. They'd move along behind the dancing bee, their antennae close to her body. After a few moments, one after another, they'd turn away abruptly and leave the hive. Some of the men who watched this phenomenon began to associate it with the appearance of a lot of bees where one had found a source of nectar.

Both beekeepers and scientists attempted to study and understand the dance. But sometimes the dance was round, sometimes it was a "wagging" dance with two alternating half circles that touched on one side. Sometimes the dances were performed quite fast, sometimes quite slowly. And the angle from the perpendicular of the touching side of the half circles seemed at various times to be any angle around the three hundred and sixty. To make the whole problem even more complicated, bees returning from a special source of nectar in the morning would dance at one angle, while bees returning from that same source in the afternoon might dance at a completely different angle. This was the sort of thing calculated to make an investigator throw up his hands in frustration, quit and go fishing.

That's how matters stood, literally for centuries, until a German scientist, Dr. Karl von Frisch, began his experiments. First he made himself a special hive. Instead of having the comb frames side by side and close, he arranged a battery of six comb frames, with two side by side on the bottom, the next two on top of them, and the other two on top of *them*. This made a huge tall hive, but very thin. The outside walls were of glass—it looked like bees between a couple of storm windows—so that you could stand there and watch the whole flat side of six comb frames at once. It was a cinch that the bees that lived in *that* house weren't going to throw stones.

Dr. von Frisch then set out a dish of sugar water and waited for a bee to find it. When she did he was ready with a tiny artist's paint brush and a dish of dry artist's pigment which had been mixed into a combination of shellac and alcohol.

When a bee appeared and got thoroughly wrapped up in filling her honey stomach with the sugar water, von Frisch daubed a tiny spot of white on the thorax, right next to the back of the head. The bee's thorax would correspond to the area covered by a short jacket on a human. Then he went to the hive and watched the frames until a bee with a white spot showed up. The bee gave her load of sugar water to another bee, as I've explained earlier; then she began her dance on the vertical comb.

She moved in a circle counterclockwise, then when she reached the point of beginning, turned and described the same circle clockwise, turned and did it all again and again.

Other bees became excited, stretched out their antennae close to her, turned abruptly and left the hive.

Meantime back at the ranch—at the feeding table, that is —unmarked bees began to show up. They'd leave the hive, circle until they found the sugar water, light and begin to fill their honey stomachs. They didn't follow the white-marked bee; many of them were there ahead of her. Which pretty well shot the idea that she "brought" them.

Von Frisch began marking all the bees that arrived at the feeding table. White next to the back of the head indicated the figure 1. Red was 2, blue was 3, yellow was 4 and green was 5. A white spot at the back of the thorax, *away* from the head, was 6, red in that area was 7, and the others in order until green represented 0. This made it possible to mark 99 bees and identify each one, to keep records about them, to time them, and to gain all sorts of information that might be useful. For instance, two yellow spots, one forward and one back, would identify bee number 49. But two yellow spots side by side up next to the head, would be bee number 44. A white spot forward and a green spot back would be bee number 10.

Then using the same five colors and painting a spot at the opposite end of the bee, down next to the stinger, using these spots to indicate hundreds, von Frisch was able to bring the total of markable bees to 599. Two yellow spots, as I said, would be 44 if placed side by side forward on the thorax. But add another yellow spot next to the stinger and you have bee number 444. It's the same principle that was used in a marked deck of cards I once owned—purely for reasons of entertainment, you understand—that employed tiny birds in different positions against one tiny mountain in the big mountain scene on the backs of the cards.

With his marking system all set up, von Frisch laboriously, painstakingly, began all sorts of experiments. If results might be read in more than one way, he carefully devised other experiments to decide which was the correct conclusion.

His first experiment was designed to see whether or not the dance in any way gave the direction of the source of supply. Von Frisch fed several numbered bees at one dish on the usual table to the west of the hive. But he placed similar dishes the same distance from the hive to the east, to the north, and to the south.

The marked bees returned to the hive and performed round dances. A few minutes later, and simultaneously, new bees appeared at all four of the feeding dishes. About the same number of bees appeared at each, though the original marked bees always returned to the dish from which they had been fed.

This was a setback. Pretty obviously that round dance told the bees nothing about direction. It just said, "Look, gals, there's a whole lot of food out there. Let's get out there fast and start bringing it back before the hive next door finds it."

But von Frisch kept on experimenting. Bees ought to be gathering from flowers, not dishes. So he picked fresh cyclamen blossoms and fed marked bees with sugar water placed on those. He also placed two large dishes at about the same distance from the hive in another direction, one containing a gorgeous display of cyclamen blossoms, the other a fine arrangement of phlox. But no sugar water on either.

The fed bees went back to the hive and danced the round dance. A few minutes later other bees appeared at the two dishes of blossoms. They crawled all over the cyclamen blossoms, as if they couldn't believe there was no food there. They paid absolutely no attention to the dish of phlox right there beside the other dish.

Just in case cyclamen might be more interesting than phlox naturally, von Frisch then fed marked bees on phlox blossoms. At once new bees appeared, crawled all over the dish of phlox, but wouldn't bother at all with the dish of cyclamen.

To make sure it was the scent they were guided by, he tried unscented blossoms of bilberry and got negative results. He next fed his marked bees from a low dish set upon a cardboard scented with peppermint oil. He placed at the same distance from the hive other similar cardboard pieces, some scented with peppermint oil, others with other oils. The bees lit all over anything that peppermint oil had touched, and ignored all other cardboard pieces.

This biological function of flower scents hadn't been known before. In gathering honey and carrying pollen from one flower to another, the bees thus stick to one species, guided by scent, don't crawl into any blossom they see beside any other, even though they may look almost alike.

To further prove his point von Frisch visited the botanical gardens in Munich when 700 different flowers were all in blossom at once. He picked out one flower, growing in one small bed, which biologists said was never visited by honeybees. He took his hive and his marked bees to a point just outside the botanical gardens, fed them on sugar water placed on blossoms of this *Helichrysum lanatum*. And within an hour many bees lighted on the flowers in that *Helichrysum* bed inside looking for food. They had picked that scent out from among the seven hundred. The attendants were astonished and tremendously impressed.

This further proved, if such proof were needed, that bees

are stubborn little insects and won't be bilked by ordinary diversions in their search for something which one of their number, in a dance, has told them exists.

Von Frisch performed thousands of experiments of this type. He fixed it so that the bees had one scent in their honey stomach, another on their bodies. He pasted something over the scent organ with which each bee is equipped back near the stinger, and which they open when they return to a rich food source to guide other bees. For many years he performed all these experiments close to the hive because it was easier, and because he could then watch both areas at once.

But as he experimented, he saw things on occasion which made him wonder if the bees weren't able actually to tell other bees the distance they must travel. So he set up one feeding station ten yards from the hive and another a little over three hundred yards from the hive. He fed his marked bees at these stations. And he became aware of a very peculiar thing. All the marked bees that came from the near station when food was plentiful did the round dance which he had come to recognize. But all bees that had been fed at the far station performed a totally different dance. It was what he began to call a "wagging" dance. They would run forward wagging their rear ends for a tiny distance.

Then they would turn left and form a half circle by coming back to the starting point. They'd run rapidly ahead, wagging their rears, then form another half circle to the right, returning again to the starting point. They'd repeat these alternating patterns over and over. Thus the common flat side of the two half circles became actually the diameter of a whole circle.

This dance was one which von Frisch had noticed many years before, but had never seen during his feeding of bees close to the hive. Since the pollen sacs on the legs of the bees that he had seen performing this dance had been full, he had jumped to the conclusion it was a dance performed by bees returning from gathering pollen. But here it cropped up again when there was no pollen—just sugar water being fed at a distance of a little over three hundred yards.

So von Frisch began to move the nearer feeding station gradually farther and farther away. At a point between 50 and 100 yards the bees, returning, gave up doing the round dance and began to do the wagging double-half-circle dance.

He began to move the far feeding station nearer, too. The same bees continued to feed there, but when he had reached a point between 100 yards and 50 yards, the returning bees gave up their wagging dance and began to do a round dance.

Then began a series of literally thousands of observations, years of painstaking, unrelenting work, some of it extremely strenuous. Gradually he moved the feeding table farther and farther away from the hive. Finally he reached a point 3.7 miles away from it.

In the course of moving the feeding station to that extreme distance (two miles is usually tops for a bee to travel to flowers for nectar) von Frisch and his assistants watched 3,885 dances of bees collecting food, from 100 yards to 3.7 miles. And in so doing they learned that the number of turns the bee made in a period of 15 seconds by the stopwatch, told the distance of the food supply from home.

Amazingly, the nearer the food was to the hive, the more turns the bee got into her dance in the 15-second period. She'd run through between nine and ten complete cycles at 100 yards, and seven at 200 yards. At half a mile she'd jitterbug through four and one-half cycles. And when the feeding table reached the 3.7-mile point the dancing bee would go through only two cycles of the dance in the 15-second period.

There was a little variability, but not much. Mostly this stemmed from the fact that the rate of dance might vary a little from colony to colony. And the wind made a difference. Von Frisch reached the conclusion that, whereas humans thought of it in terms of yards, the bees figured it in terms of the amount of effort needed to get there. Thus a dance would be different when the bees were bucking a head wind than it would be on a day when they had a tail wind.

All this showed how the bees told each other the distance to go. But it didn't solve the question of whether they got across the exact direction.

Von Frisch fed marked bees on a scented card 200 yards or more south of the hive. And then he set out similar cards, scented the same, without food. Some were near the original card, some at varying distances away from that card, but all were the same distances from the hive.

After his marked bees had been fed, within a few minutes bees appeared at the feeding place, and a lesser number at the cards right close to it. But no bees appeared at the cards in other directions. Somehow those bees were getting across a pretty accurate compass directive to their co-workers. They were flying exactly in the direction they were supposed to fly.

This was a completely astonishing conclusion. But there was no other conclusion that he could come to. Like all scientists, he was consumed with curiosity to know how they did it.

So he fed more bees and watched more dances. And he found that marked bees returning from a given feeding station, all danced in such a way that the straight part of their "wagging" dance—the part that began it, the part between the forming of the half circles—always pointed in one direction.

But when he was operating two stations with marked bees, one to the south, one to the north, the bees that had been fed to the south would dance in the opposite direction from those that had been fed to the north. The bees to the south of the hive would dance toward the left on the vertical comb; the bees to the north would dance to the right.

Furthermore, if von Frisch kept on feeding these bees all day and kept on watching their dances, the dances would change very gradually, but very definitely. In the late afternoon the bees would be dancing in an entirely different direction from the direction of their morning dance, even though they were still feeding at the same place. But both north and south dances would change in relationship to each other and would still be in opposite directions.

Other scientists had shown that both bees and ants used the sun for a compass in territory where landmarks were few and far between. Von Frisch, remembering this, became convinced that his bees were using the angle of the sun as a basis for their directions. This was the most logical way to account for the change in direction between morning and afternoon. But there again, how were they doing it? They were dancing on the face of a vertical comb. There had to be a translation there. And they were flying on cloudy days when there was no sun.

More experiments; a lot more. Von Frisch took a comb out and laid it flat while a bee was dancing on it. Immediately the dance changed to the exact direction of the feeding station. Set the comb vertical again and the dance went back to the direction it had been before. This still could be the angle of the sun to the line of flight. Because once horizontal, the direction of flight and the angle of the flight from the sun, of course became exactly the same.

He decided that the perpendicular or the force of gravity, represented the direction of the sun from the hive. If the direction of the sun and the direction of the feeding station from the hive were at a 60-degree angle from each other, and the feeding station was to the left of the sun, the bees coming from there would dance at a 60-degree angle to the left of perpendicular. If the feeding station was 120 degrees to the right of the direction of the sun from the hive, the bees coming from there would dance at a 120-degree angle to the right of perpendicular. If the hive was directly between the feeding station and the sun, the bees would dance straight down.

This was an astonishing and amazing conclusion, that bees had in the course of their existence and evolution, chosen straight up to designate the direction of the sun. And that those tiny insects, using that as a point of departure, were every day figuring dozens of complicated angles that would have made a geometry student turn pale.

Von Frisch must have felt a little the way Columbus felt when he suggested that the world was round when anybody in his right mind could see that it was flat. He knew that nobody would believe him until he'd repeated his experiments over and over for other scientists, or until those scientists, using his methods plus any other tests they might personally come up with, had experimented extensively for themselves. He said once, "No competent scientist *ought* to believe these things on first hearing."

But he had confidence in the work he had done, so he publicized his work and his findings. The repercussions in the scientific world were actually a little better than he had expected they would be. His reputation as a scientist was so secure that most of the scientists didn't say it wasn't so. But still a great skepticism prevailed everywhere.

One Englishman said that the whole idea was too fantastic and too absurd for anyone to believe, and that he would cross the English Channel and face von Frisch and tell him so. When he reached Munich von Frisch told him to feed marked bees in any direction from the special hive, at any distance he felt like feeding them. He wasn't to let anybody know where he had fed them. When the bees returned and danced, von Frisch would tell him exactly in what direction and how far away the feeding had taken place.

The Englishman started out to prove once and for all that bees just couldn't be bright enough to figure out angles, remember them until they got outside the hive, and then relate the angle to the position of the sun. And fly in the right direction. Absurd. He fed the bees, returned confidently to the hive only to have von Frisch tell him exactly where he had fed them.

On the theory that the thing still couldn't happen, therefore somebody must have seen the feeding or the direction he had taken, he was very careful the next time not to be seen. He was confident that, without being obvious enough about it so that feelings would be hurt, he had fooled everybody about where the feeding took place.

When he returned to the hive von Frisch told him exactly where the feeding station had been located. After several days and a lot more experiments, the Englishman went home again, completely convinced and high in his praise of von Frisch.

Meantime von Frisch tackled the problem of how the bees knew where the sun was on a cloudy day. Bees have an exceptional memory for time, and if you feed bees between ten and eleven at a certain place for several days, they will return between ten and eleven for several days afterward, after you have taken the food away. Von Frisch thought perhaps they could remember where the sun was in relation to landmarks near the hive and could therefore correctly *remember* its position at any given time for their dance on a cloudy day.

But when he took his hive far away into unfamiliar country on a cloudy day, they still danced correctly when fed. Somehow they could see something in the sky that humans could not see, which gave them the sun's direction. After years of painstaking experiments he decided that the bee eye is able to recognize the polarization of light—like a Nicol prism or a piece of polaroid. He was still experimenting with this and hoping to prove it definitely when he made public his findings on the language of the bees.

He found, too, that the dances were used in the same way by the scouts sent out to find a new home at the time of swarming. They would return and dance for the swarm hanging on the tree limb, to tell the hive members and the queen the location of a possible new home, its distance and direction.

In the chapter on swarming we've seen that the energy and persistence with which the returning scout carried out the dance seemed to be in direct relation to how suitable for bee housekeeping the scout felt that the place would be that she had found. The scouts that were not too sure would watch a very energetic and persistent dance, go and examine the place for themselves. And if it was better than theirs, would come back and dance for it instead.

In every case, then, the communication dance turned out to be the basis for the picking of a new home. Von Frisch watched until he could tell exactly where every swarming colony intended to locate.

One of the von Frisch assistants visited the college town where I live, and he told an amazing story about an incident during the experiments on swarming bees and their scouts. He swore it was a true incident, and that he had participated in it.

At the University of Munich the scouts from a swarm returned and danced and were observed by the von Frisch team. One dance was particularly persistent; other bees went and located the proposed home site, returned and danced enthusiastically. It became apparent this was to be the place.

Von Frisch translated the dance into human terms and told his assistants just where the site was located. They jumped on their bicycles and tore away to be at the spot when the bees arrived. Much to their astonishment the directions, taken from the bees, led deep into the city, not out into the country as they had anticipated.

In fact, to the best of their ability to follow the directions, the spot was on the railroad square in the heart of Munich. They stopped there beside a sidewalk coffee shop and talked the situation over. They were sure they were right, but they were shaken by the apparent scarcity of bee-housing opportunities in a city square.

The proprietor, seeing them loitering there beside his establishment, came out and asked them what they were doing.

One of the assistants said, "We're just waiting for some bees."

No sooner had he spoken than there came the usual loud humming and the bees arrived. It became apparent at once that they had chosen a round hole in the cornice of the coffee shop which obviously had a large hollow behind it. But twenty-five thousand or more bees can't all go through a small hole at once.

So the loud humming was all-encompassing, and the bees were zooming everywhere. The customers, sipping coffee at sidewalk tables, overturned the chairs and the tables in their haste to get out of there. Women screamed. Men ran. The excitement was fantastic.

The proprietor took one horrified look and ran for the telephone and called the police. "There are," he said, "a bunch of college boys playing a trick on me with a bunch of bees. I don't know how they're doing it, but they are. They mentioned bees. It's them all right."

The police came and arrested the von Frisch assistants and took them off to the pokey. Von Frisch himself had to come down and explain the whole thing at great length before he was able to get them released.

There must have been many unexpected turns and happenings like this during all those years of laborious experiments. They must have made the work pretty exciting at times. At others it must have been deadly dull and extremely discouraging.

But however it was, the world of science and the world of bee culture, owes a tremendous debt to von Frisch for proving that bees work by smelling as well as by seeing. And that they can communicate to the other members of the colony the fact of housing or food, its exact direction and distance. This is the story of the discovery of the language of the bees.

9

COLONY LIFE IN WINTER

Bees are unlike ants in that their wintering is by no stretch of the imagination a hibernation. They're a cold-blooded creature, it's true, better able to stand cold than warm-blooded humans. But if their body temperature sinks to 27 degrees Fahrenheit, they die; 43 degrees they can stand for extended periods.

So they can't hibernate and must remain warmer than the zero air around them. They move and eat during even the coldest winter just as we do. Yet we have clothing and central heating, and fuel bills and they don't. The amazing part is that a nice warm heated hive, representing great creature comfort for the bees, would be the worst thing that could happen to them. I'll get to that in a moment.

There are roughly three types of winter operation in the apiary world. First, there is the normal wintering in the North, where temperatures may go down below zero and the bees live on stored honey. There is no apiary activity there for months. Second, there is wintering in the South's warm climates where bees fly all year, and the period when no honey is coming in is either short or nonexistent. And third, there is the winter operation that combines the two. This last is migratory beekeeping, and means packing up the colonies, loading them aboard a truck, and driving them south for a tupelo or some other honeyflow in a warm climate, then repacking them for the trip back to their northern stand and a clover or fruit honeyflow there.

The first type of wintering is mostly a matter of preparation. In a hollow tree, the bees get ready for the cold winter up North themselves, to the best of their ability. As we have seen, they gather as much honey and pollen as possible, glue everything up shipshape with propolis. Then they form a cluster and hope for the best.

In an apiary the beekeeper helps them. The emphasis there is on colony strength. This is the most important help he can give. He will check, too, their honey supply, and if it is inadequate, will give them more food. He will, if he's a commercial beekeeper, give them capped honey frames which he has taken from some other colony. Or he will feed them sugar water.

The biggest percentage of beekeepers today use the double or two-story hive. Some beekeepers with an exceptionally strong colony, even use a three-story hive. The two-story hive should contain at least sixty pounds of capped honey. This should carry the colony nicely through even a long severe winter. The total weight of such a hive would be a little over double the stored honey weight, or about 130 pounds. The beekeeper will try to have spots of unfilled comb in the second story because bees like to make a cluster on filled comb around such an unfilled area. He will, too, try to guess where the bees will be by brood-rearing time and place pollen so it will be easily available to the cluster then. Beekeepers are an experimental lot, and each has his own ideas about how the stores in a hive should be set up for maximum colony good in winter.

The beekeeper will also make sure he has some sort of windbreak to protect his colony, possibly a wooden fence made in sections with braces not posts, so that if he moves his apiary he can move the fence, too. It shouldn't be a solid fence because then the wind will sweep up and over it and down onto the bees. Large cracks between the boards will stop this. Then he will wrap the hive in black tar paper (black because black will absorb the rays of the sun) in some design he himself has figured out. Or he will place an outer box around each hive with straw or some other loose insulation in between the outer and inner walls, or move the colonies into a cellar. Not a house cellar, but one dug in the ground for just this purpose where the colonies can be stored in long rows three or four colonies high.

He will bore (or unplug) a one-inch hole in the upper part of the hive to let moisture escape. If he has insulated the hive, he will run a pipe of some sort through the insulated area to the outside. The bees eat honey and in doing so change it into carbon dioxide and water. The water, a huge amount by volume, is given off in the hive and if there is no way for it to escape outside, the combs will mold, and the colony may succumb to dysentery and other ills.

The hole in the upper part of the hive acts also as an upper entrance. Snow or ice or both may block the bottom entrance for a while. Without a second entrance the bees would soon die. The owner will also make sure his hives are not placed at the bottom of a hollow where there will be no airflow to take away moisture. He usually tries for a side hill, sunny, facing south. Or a sunny area protected by farm buildings.

When the temperature drops low the bees will form their

cluster, and this is one of the most amazing things in the world of nature.

The cluster is designed to combat the cold. It is a loose ball of bees formed in the spaces between, and in the empty cells of the regular combs. There is an outside crust of bees from one to three inches thick. The rest of the bees are inside and they provide heat for the cluster. The bees inside the cluster are not as close-packed as the crust.

The cluster temperature may drop as low as 57 degrees inside, and run from there up into the 90's. The outside crust will range from 46 to 43 degrees. When it gets down into the 43-degree body temperature area, the cluster will combat this change in two ways. The bees inside the cluster will generate more heat by motion, and the cluster itself will contract to bring less surface in contact with the cold and more bees inside the crust to produce heat. When the temperature outside rises again, the cluster will expand accordingly. Thus it is obvious why a strong colony and a big cluster winters best. They've got more little radiators inside that cluster than a weak swarm with comparatively few bees.

In my youth it was thought that the outside bees, when they grew uncomfortably cold, burrowed into the cluster, and bees that were warm and contented and in no mood to fight about it, allowed themselves to be pushed to the outer crust. It has now been pretty thoroughly proved that there is out and in movement, but that it is far slower than the above would imply. The outside bees can remain at 43-degree body temperature for a long time. But they must have food. When the food in their honey stomachs is gone, they move inside the cluster to replenish this food, and other fed bees find themselves in the outside crust.

As long as the feet of an outside bee are in contact with the mass of her sisters, the temperature inside the hive can be below zero and the bee will be fine. But if you lift one of those bees by the wings clear of the cluster, almost instantly she will freeze to death. Occasionally the cluster contracts too fast for several of the outside bees to keep up with it, and they die for their carelessness.

Inside the cluster, in the fall when the temperature goes down, the cluster temperature will go down, too. But when the hive temperature gets to 57 degrees, a change takes place and the bees begin to be active and produce heat. They fan for coolness in summer, and then fan for heat there inside the cluster in winter.

Below the 57-degree point the temperature changes according to inverse ratio. If the outside temperature continues to drop, the temperature clear inside the cluster continues to rise to offset it, and keep the outside hard-packed crust of bees supplied with heat. Other insects that hibernate become less active as the temperature goes lower and lower. But bees grow more active as the temperature lowers, to produce heat.

That, briefly, is how the cluster keeps itself warm. When the temperature rises, and the sun beats on the hive, the cluster expands, and some of the bees even fly out on brief flights, rid themselves of their feces and return. Some are lost on these expeditions should the sun suddenly disappear under a cloud and the bees be caught in quick-dropping temperatures.

Such a temperature rise also provides the cluster a chance to shift away from eaten-out comb over onto full comb, in readiness for the next temperature drop.

In February when there is generally more and brighter sun and therefore more warm periods in the hive, the laying of eggs by the queen will start. If there is pollen available inside the cluster, the resulting brood will be raised to maturity. This will, to some extent, serve to replace the individuals that die off.

But, you say, how simple it would be to have little electric heaters in each hive, and let the bees have a warm, pleasant winter, instead of one in which some of them are chilled to a 43-degree body temperature compared to our 98.6.

Well, as you must have guessed, all sorts of experiments toward this end have been tried, because humans are very softhearted. And up to now the experiments have pretty much failed.

The reason for the failure is very basic. You warm the hive and the bees want to fly abroad. The moment they emerge into a zero day they drop as if they were hit with a science-fiction disintegrator ray. You'd lose your colony in no time.

If that is the case, you say, at least you could insulate the hive very heavily to hold the inside temperature up. This too just doesn't work well. To be sure, the temperature does go down slower inside the hive, but given a three- or four-day cold spell, the inside temperature will go just as low as it would have without the insulation. And then when a sunny day comes, it doesn't warm up quickly. Bees needing to fly out and relieve themselves don't do so, and dysentery can result. The next cold spell comes along before the bees have had any sort of warm respite.

Put the bees in a cellar with a furnace, and they'll fly out and around the cellar all winter. A cellar is damp anyway; add a few colonies of bees with no outside ventilation and it will get much damper. Dysentery again. If you have no furnace, the temperature will go down below the 43-degree mark and just stay there, with no warm-up periods. A temperature-controlled, scientifically vented cellar, specially dug for bees, is the best answer in very cold far north areas. This, too, has its drawbacks, the main one being that the colonies have to be carried in there, and are jarred and upset when this is done. If you take part of the colonies out ahead of the rest, in the spring, the ones who get settled first are likely to rob-out the ones still dazed with the change from dark to light.

More and more beekeepers, in areas where the temperatures go to sixty below zero and stay below zero for extended periods, as we told you, are killing off their bees with gas in the fall, sealing up the hives, and then buying packages of bees-with-queen for each hive the next spring. This is expensive. But no more expensive, they say, than trying to winter their bees, sometimes with poor success.

The hives could, of course, be electrically heated and thermostat-controlled so that they would remain about 45-degrees no matter how cold it got outside. This, too, would be expensive. And the system would have to be foolproof or the bees would die as the result of any unexpected mechanical failure. An ordinary power failure would not necessarily be disastrous, because the bees could then handle themselves in the normal, time-honored way. But a failure of the mechanism to shut off the heat properly would have all the colony venturing out to their deaths. In addition, many apiaries and nearly all outyards don't have any electricity available.

Up to now, as far as I know, there has been no accepted setup for providing winter warmth to the bees. And too much insulation, experiments have shown, just puts the bees in cold storage. They get along best with wind breaks, tar paper, and a sunny southern slope.

At first blush you would think the beekeeper in warmer territory would be far better off than his northern brother who must cope with all these problems we have just explored.

He may very well be better off, but he has a few problems, too. First of these is that in many southern locations the beekeeper harvests nowhere near as much surplus honey as the northern beekeeper does. He'll be lucky if he can average half as much per colony as his beekeeper friend in a good area up North averages.

In addition he must contend with more and stickier propolis than the bees gather in the North. The wax moth can riddle his combs year-round instead of just during the summer. And wax moths burrowing as larvae and growing and becoming moths and laying eggs and burrowing some more, without having to lie dormant during the cold months, can ruin a fantastic amount of comb in an incredibly short time. The honey the beekeeper raised will be more amber in color, and stronger in flavor than northern clover and al- falfa honey, and he may have to sell it for a cent or two a pound less. There are more snakes, more spiders, more ants, more dragonflies. And the summer heat and sun load is so great that open sheds must be built if no natural shade is available.

In addition there are two other problems: flooding at cer- tain times of the year in low-lying sections, and grass fires. Owners often clear their land by firing it.

These matters are not hard to defend against. But to do so costs money. The hives in the lowlands of some north Florida rivers must be placed on platforms sometimes as much as ten feet above the ground. For nominal flooding, long platforms a couple or three feet above the ground will do the trick. These same platforms, or possibly hive stands of about the same height, will defend against grass fires, too.

But nothing can defend against having the field bee try to return to the hive site when there's a raging inferno all around the home stand. At best she will have to remain away a long time, until the fire passes and the area cools. She may have a lot of trouble doing this.

Or at worst, she may have her wings singed by the unexpected heat and be lost. All nectar for the bees in the burned-over area, except in flowering trees, is lost until new growth comes up.

To make up for the lower honey yield per hive down south, the beekeepers there have many of them taken to raising package bees and queens, as we have noted earlier. It is time here to examine that huge, fast-growing industry in more detail.

Beekeepers in the South have found this packaging of bees extremely lucrative. Their bees start egg laying and brood rearing early for their honeyflow while the North is still blanketed with snow. In this they are encouraged in every possible way by the beekeeper.

Along about the 15th of April the beekeeper makes up his packages of bees according to his orders received. The three-pound package is the bread-and-butter package.

He has a specially built funnel the size of a standard hive, with drone and queen excluders set in the narrow part. He puts the hive body in this, shakes it with a series of sudden jars. The bees tumble down into the funnel and through between the bars of the queen excluder into the package below. The package is on a scale. The package will lose from one to seven ounces in transit depending on how much honey each bee had in her honey stomach. A bee can carry roughly her own weight in honey. Usually the reputable shipper adds about seven ounces to insure full weight upon arrival. The three-pound package contains roughly 10,000 bees. Mostly these bees will be young, vigorous bees because the majority of the bees inside a hive would be young hive bees.

The standard package itself is made up of a wooden top

and bottom, with wooden corner pieces. But all sorts of other packages have been devised. The sides and ends are made of screening. The hole in the top of this shipping case just fits the mouth, or small end, of the funnel. The container for sugar water also just passes through this hole. The funnel is removed when the package weighs the right amount, the bees are shaken down, the syrup jar and a queen cage inserted (if it is to be shipped with queen) and the whole thing sealed and shipped.

The reason the industry built up so fast was purely financial on both ends of the operation. Those far-northern apiary owners we spoke of who kill their bees with gas, or kill the queen and let the colony die out naturally, began this practice because of fantastic wintering losses that would sometimes leave 75 percent of their hives vacant for a year when a particularly bad winter had taken its toll. Two bad winters in a row could wipe out a beekeeper completely. Here was a ready-made market for packaged bees. The far-north beekeeper grasped the opportunity eagerly.

Then the beekeeper who could ordinarily winter his colonies pretty well, found that when some of them did die out, he could buy packages and still reap a nice harvest instead of simply saying, "Next year may be better." He experimented and found, too, that if a colony was very weak from wintering, they would spend the whole summer working back up to strength and would leave him no honey excess. So for those colonies he bought one- or two-pound packages of bees (*without* queens) to strengthen the colony. And this worked far above even his highest hopes. The young, strong bees in packages with queens and without, put his apiary in top shape before his honeyflow, and paid off in dollars.

On the other end, the southern beekeeper found that he

could make far more by packaging bees and raising queens, and making what honey he could besides, than he could in averaging the smaller amount per-hive-per-year that most southern areas will produce. He may have had a bad moment or two in thinking he might be helping Damyankees. But he salved his conscience with a trip to the bank, and the hope that his bees would roundly sting their northern purchasers.

Thus a new industry was born and has grown. To me it is simply amazing that man has learned to manipulate these weaponed insects to such an extent that he can raise a lot of queens, breed them, sometimes artificially, ship their sexless sisters by the pound all over the United States with them, and cause little physical damage to them. Or for that matter to the manipulator in preparing them. In its way this progress in bee culture is almost as astonishing as putting a man in orbit. And needs almost as much specialized scientific know-how.

Beekeeping for honey in the winter in the South, for the most part, betters the colony average only in areas where there is some special agricultural crop to work. Or where there is some natural southern tree or bush, like the tupelo or mangrove, that blooms in quantity and keeps the bees extremely busy for several weeks.

The crop areas are the irrigated areas like those of California, Arizona, Texas, Mexico and Florida, and the rich black dirt areas of some southern states, notably Florida, where the mucklands have been drained by many long canals so that crops can be raised. Bees do well on these croplands, especially the irrigated land in California on which alfalfa is grown. But the tupelo trees and the orange groves of Florida provide spectacular runs—so spectacular, in fact, that the northerners have looked with envy on their southern brothers and decided that they wanted part of the almost limitless sweet nectar for their own bees. This takes us to migratory beekeeping.

Migratory beekeeping started, incredible as it seems, more than three thousand years before Christ. Written records prove it. The place was Egypt, and the practice was common there. The upper Egypt season was earlier than the season in lower Egypt. So beekeepers would place their bees aboard rafts on the Nile River in the upper reaches. The bees could fly to nectar from the rafts just as handily as they could from land. When the honeyflow slowed, the beekeepers would pull up the anchor or cast off the mooring, and drift to better flowers as warmer weather came gradually to the area further from the equator.

In our country the first migratory beekeeping over any distance was attempted with the help of railroads. A team of horses and a wagon would have been too slow, the roads were too bumpy, and the wagon springs were very little help.

But trucks changed all that. Theoretically, now you can harvest a crop of clover honey in Vermont, take a huge trailer truck (or several) loaded with hives to Florida, harvest tupelo or orange blossom crops, and have your bees back in Vermont in time for the apple blossoms there.

Practically, though, this isn't as easy as it sounds. To begin with, there's the cost. Your bees may stand the trip if loaded and packed right. But your pocketbook may not stand the expense of so long a journey. A trailer truck round trip of 3,500 miles, especially if you don't own the trailer truck and have to hire it, will mean a terrific expense. There'll be labor, too, and food, and the cost of a site from which to operate.

There are a lot of southern beekeepers. They are fine citizens. But they take a dim view of Yankee encroachment on what they consider their preserves, especially if they think there's only about enough nectar for their own bees. Northerners trying to get a foothold have found hive sites hard to rent or very expensive.

There are tupelo areas and mangrove areas that could handle perhaps ten times, perhaps twenty times, the bees that are in the area. But tupelo and mangrove areas are swampy. The local beekeepers build those long platforms on stilts that we talked about, for their hives. A beekeeper from the north has to lease swampland to build his own, or force his bees to take nectar only from the edge of the swamp. One course runs up his expenses, the other cuts down on his take.

So practically, migratory beekeeping is carried on mostly with trucks, over minor distances with a careful eye on expenses. The beekeepers who migrate with their hives to Florida are likely to be from stands in nearby states and not from, say, New England. In California, migratory beekeeping is very strong indeed. There the beekeepers move their hives twenty-five miles, possibly fifty miles, to pick up some particular honeyflow where the farmer or rancher will welcome them with open arms on account of pollination. By moving only a few miles, these men can pick up a crop of orange blossom honey, then sage honey, then honey from huge bean fields or some other crop, and then clover or alfalfa crops.

Beekeepers come from neighboring states to California in the fall, build up their colonies on eucalyptus in the winter, then pick up an orange blossom crop, then a sage crop, and then move the bees back home in time for their regular run of clover and alfalfa.

Even a trip of as little as five miles to a huge buckwheat field, or to an apple orchard, may make all the difference between a fine crop and a dismal one. Charles Mraz in winter sometimes travels without bees to Mexico to help a Mexican beekeeper pack and move his hives some sixty miles to catch a citrus honey crop. It gives him an expenses-paid winter trek, and gets the Mexican a highly trained helper.

The main consideration in packing bees for a journey, long or short, is ventilation. Some beekeepers remove the covers from their hives in preparation, and replace them with a prepared rectangular screen top from four to six inches high. The screen top has corner posts heavy enough so that when other hives are stacked on top of it, it will be strong enough to hold them. There should be space between the rows of hives for ventilation, and then those screen covers will give four to six inches of ventilation from all four sides, in transit.

Ideally, the hives should be loaded at night. But in a big operation this is impossible, so the entrance slits should have a screen insert affixed during the night when all the bees are inside. Thus you take your full colony with you the next day; none will be coming back from the fields to find the hive gone. Some beekeepers move short distances without closing the entrance.

Extensive experiments have proved that bees can stand the sun and daytime heat without trouble if there is sufficient ventilation. But cut off the ventilation for any reason, and they may very well succumb even though the day does not seem particularly warm. If the regular top is left on the hive and inadequate top ventilation provided, the bees can and do sometimes mass across the screen which closes off the entrance slit at the bottom, and thus without meaning to they cut off circulation and doom the colony. In moving bees any distance, massive ventilation is imperative.

Moving bees a considerable distance is actually better than moving them only twenty-five or thirty feet. When the colony is opened in the new area the bees will see at once upon emerging that the surroundings are changed, and will note their landmarks with minutest care before setting out for the fields. But if the hive is moved only a few feet, the bees may not notice any change when they emerge, and may return to the old stand, find no hive and be lost to the colony. Particularly this is true of Italian bees.

Thus we see that the bees in the North have a rugged time in winter. Their problems can be lessened by careful building up and manipulation on the part of their owner. But heat, indoor storage or heavy insulation can spell out a death warrant for the colony members if the greatest care is not exercised. Southern bees have it much easier, and whole colonies of bees, whole apiaries even, go to Florida or California for the winter for business reasons just as the tired businessman from New York goes to a long convention in Miami.

10

DISEASES AND ENEMIES

You would think that any insect equipped with such an efficient defense weapon would be able to master almost any enemy, and handle almost any situation. Probably bees could do just that if all attacks were frontal, and the full force of fifty thousand sharp stingers with their sacs of poison could be brought to bear. Unfortunately for them, this is not always possible.

A case in which those stingers can't all be brought to bear, is against one. One bear, that is. And the pun is definitely intended.

The fur coat of one of these huge honey-lovers is heavy enough, and the hide under it is thick enough, to frustrate a would-be hive defender. Mostly she can't get close enough to the bear's hide to ram her stinger home.

Don't get the idea that even under these optimum conditions a bear has matters all his own way, however. There are always the eyes, and that very defenseless and tender nose. Bees don't waste a lot of frustrated time on the coat; the greatest number swarm all over the face.

A friend of mine, who is a fine hunter, was hired by a beekeeper to get rid of a bear that was ruining a beeyard by coming down from the nearby mountain at night and breaking up one hive at a time.

My friend set himself with his rifle, a thermos of coffee, and some sandwiches, to watch all night. It was bright moonlight, and he sat against the trunk of a big tree where he'd be in the shadows and where the wind would not blow from him toward the beeyard.

In spite of himself, sometime after midnight he dozed off. He gradually became conscious of a yipping and squealing. The bear had entered the yard, knocked apart the nearest hive. There in the moonlight he sat on his haunches, his hind legs spread wide on each side of the main part of the hive, holding it against his stomach with one front paw, and scooping gobs of honey and brood into his mouth with the other. The shape of his head was indistinct, so great was the cloud of angry bees around it.

And as he gorged himself he whimpered constantly in pain. And every few seconds he let out a loud yelp of real anguish. But so great was his love of honey, and especially of brood, that doggedly he kept eating in spite of the torture he was enduring. My friend took careful aim and ended the life of the thief. When next morning he examined the body, the cheeks, the nose, the eyelids even, were literally white with the poison sacs of bee stingers embedded there. Often a bear will carry part of the hive away into the woods before he gorges. By this maneuver he loses the bulk of the defenders and can enjoy his spoils in comparative peace.

The kingbird and bee martin are honey-lovers that the bee can't cope with successfully. Most birds leave bees strictly alone. If a bee sting, with its poison, can badly affect a six-foot human and cause his flesh to swell, it is easy to imagine the effect a sting has on a bird only a few inches long.

But stings and poison don't affect the kingbird or bee martin. The bee martin works in midair. But the kingbird will sit on a branch close to a beeyard, or in a direct line between a clover or buckwheat field and beehives, and flutter out to nab a homeward-returning, laden, and slow-flying worker every few seconds. There are two schools of thought on whether he gets the usual bird meal of good nourishing insect, or only mashes the body to get the juices and discards it. But all experts agree that the drop of nectar being carried, a sort of dessert, is the main attraction. He can kill a tremendous number of bees in a lifetime, and thus beekeepers hate kingbirds.

Skunks are a fairly successful bee predator. They work at night. They'll scratch at the entrance of a hive, and gobble the worker guards that come out to investigate, about as fast as they appear. The skunk gets stung, but this doesn't seem to affect him, at least in small doses. It's hard to tell, though, whether it is a knowledge of definite physical limitations in this area, or only the instinct to work at night, that mostly causes a skunk to avoid a direct daytime challenge to vast numbers of his victims.

A colony of ants, especially in southern states, sometimes attacks and exterminates a hive of bees. Seldom, though, is the attack of a daytime one.

The ants may discover a spread joint in the back of the hive, made by the warping of the wood. If no such opportunity exists, they'll try to overpower the guards suddenly, always at night. They try to get as many of their number inside before the alarm is given as possible. They fan out, keeping a tight phalanx formation. And by the time bees discover their presence, they have hundreds, maybe thousands inside, with more pouring in under protection of that phalanx formation.

The bees fight. But the ants are not nice, ethical, Marquis of Queensbury insect-against-insect warriors. Each ant freezes to a bee leg or wing and gnaws it off, and after losing several appendages the helpless victim drops to the hive bottom, harmless. Ants are stung to death, fought to death, but more move into their places and the phalanx rolls on. The frontal attack may take several nights, each weakening the colony. The rear attack is usually successful at once. When all resistance is overcome, a fantastic two-way line of ants carries the spoils of their battle away.

It's not a pleasant situation even to contemplate, and fortunately, if the beekeeper is on his job and has used carbon bisulphide or some other chemical against ant colonies near his beeyard, it happens very seldom.

Mice are a menace; a good beekeeper scatters mouse poison around his hives. Mice destroy comb, disorganize the colony. Even if they are stung to death, the body remains a problem since it is too big for the bees to move, and the stench and contamination of decay must be handled some other way. A chipmunk or squirrel which blunders into a hive in a hollow tree presents the same problem. The bees handle it neatly, even though it takes a lot of bee-hours.

They encase the carcass in propolis; entomb the dead rodent in a hard, shiny coffin which handles the matter of stench and contamination efficiently. I have found such a brown shiny hump inside a bee tree, opened it and exposed the skeleton of a small mammal.

Spiders are both friends and enemies of the beekeeper. If they are allowed to spin webs at or near bee entrances, they will catch, kill and eat a lot of bees. A lot of spiders can hurt a weak colony. But on the other side of the coin, if they are allowed to spin webs in the storage areas of the honey house where empty combs and frames are kept, the beekeeper's fight against the wax moth, which we're going to take up within a few paragraphs, will be immeasurably furthered because the spiders will catch and eat all the wax moths that fly around in there.

The "devil's darning needle," or "dragon fly" or "mosquito hawk," is one of those unbelievable bee enemies. In southern states, and especially in Florida, these insects are so numerous in April or May that the sky is sometimes black with them. Their method of capturing a bee in flight is the fantastic part. They range over a flying bee and use their cupped legs as a scoop net to entrap it. They appear in greatest numbers near rivers and swamps, where they breed. And when they are around in tremendous numbers, the bees will often stay right inside the hive, somehow knowing that to fly to the fields as usual is to sign their own death warrants. These insects can do thousands of dollars' worth of damage to a large apiary in just a few days. They can weaken all the colonies in an entire area.

Small-boy, would-be baseball pitchers armed with rocks sometimes pose a bee menace. But definitely not always with impunity, especially if they wait around at all to view the satisfying, boiling consternation of a direct hit.

Even an insect as small as a bee has its own louse. The adults perch on the back of a bee and feed on nectar or honey from her mouth parts. This louse is called *Braula coeca,* and isn't in large numbers, nor does it do much damage except as it is heavy to carry around, and a nuisance to the bee as she goes about her work. The damage comes from the larvae which tunnel in the cappings of the comb after they hatch out from an egg laid there while the work of capping is going on.

The wax moth, on the other hand, is much more prevalent and does far, far more damage. It is sometimes light in color, sometimes dark, depending on the color of the food it has eaten. It lives on wax. If it has eaten from discolored comb which has been in the hive a long time, it is dark in color. If it has eaten new, light-colored wax, it is light in color. The adult moth is perhaps three-quarters of an inch in length with a wingspread of another half inch more than its length. The female is a little larger than the male, and she can be identified easily because the female snout projects more than the male's, like a beak.

This female starts laying eggs within a few days after her birth, and lives about three weeks. In that time she averages about a hundred eggs a week. The hatching time on these varies almost unbelievably. This is due to heat or cold. In very warm weather they'll hatch out in less than a week. But in cold weather it can take more than a month.

The same variation in time of development in the larva and pupa stage is the result of warm or cold weather. On hatching out, the larvae tunnel immediately into the wax and head for the heavy partition that divides the comb into two sets of cells. The process of tunneling and growing can go on for anywhere from a month to five months, depending on the temperature. The larva starts at an eighth of an inch, grows to an inch, then spins a cocoon and stays in it anywhere from a week to many weeks depending again on the temperature. If the thermometer goes below 45 degrees, either larva or pupa becomes dormant. When the insect emerges it is a moth and, if it is a female, starts right in on the egg-laying routine, so that we've gone full cycle.

Here again the main damage is to comb. An inch-long insect burrowing around in it can do tremendous damage. And if there are a lot of them at work in there, comb walls can become so weakened that whole areas may collapse under the weight of a lot of honey.

But by far the worst disaster that can attack a colony is a disease known as Foul Brood. You can't sting a disease. This is a terrible scourge for a colony of bees. It's like a smallpox epidemic among the early settlers of our country. It is bad enough when it is the European Foul Brood, but many times worse if it is the American Foul Brood which, if it runs unchecked through a bee yard, infecting colony after colony, can wipe out all the colonies for miles around.

Foul Brood is a communicable disease, spread by a microorganism called a bacillus. This bacillus is a rod-shaped bacterium. It is carried into the hive in food, usually in honey, and is spread that way. It is in honey that the bacillus enters the body of the larva. And it starts immediately feeding on this plump, honey-fed little grub from the inside. As it feeds, it gives off wastes or toxins, and these do damage in addition to the damage done by the feeding.

But what, you'd wonder, could one microscopic little organism do to a whole colony of better than fifty thousand bees?

Well, suddenly there isn't just one. Any that have entered that larva begin in a matter of minutes to eat and to divide. Immediately there are two where there was one. These eat, grow and divide, and there are four where there were two, eight where there were four, sixteen where there were eight. In an amazingly short time there are thousands, then millions, all eating and giving off wastes. They feed and multiply, paralyze the muscles of the larva until it dies and shrinks and decays. The older bacilli reach the end of their life span, and die, and give off more poison. The decaying mass takes on the most horrible putrid odor imaginable.

This is the way Foul Brood attacks. Unless the beekeeper has a head cold to end all head colds, he can tell easily that something is amiss in the hive. If his colony is strong, the

European disease can be fought and cured providing it hasn't had too much of a start and the infection isn't too general.

The black bees (originally from Europe and called German bees, as we've seen) seem to have no ability to resist this disease. The yellow-banded Italian bees resist it very strongly and successfully. So if the beekeeper's infected colony is German, he should requeen with a strong Italian queen. Too, the queen should be caged for about two weeks and thus kept from laying eggs. And since there will be no eggs, the workers will spend their hive-time cleaning out the cells that have housed dead and diseased larvae, polishing them and getting them ready for eggs. When the beekeeper releases his queen the cells will be ready for eggs that will grow uninfected brood.

With American Foul Brood (AFB) there isn't even that much chance for the beekeeper to help and to manipulate a cure. There's *no* chance, except through early diagnosis and ruthless destruction of infected comb and brood, and the use of great care to see that no honey from an infected hive is placed or spilled where bees from other hives can carry it home. Honey from an infected hive should be destroyed, not extracted or sold, even though the bacillus does not affect humans. Most honey houses aren't completely beeproof, and even a tiny drop of infected honey carried home to another hive by one of its workers can start the cycle again, and possibly infect dozens more colonies before it can finally be stamped out in that apiary.

Both American and European Foul Brood introduced in food attack the larva in its early stages, usually in its first day of life. The older the larva grows, the less susceptible it becomes to attack from the bacillus. After the third day of the life of the larva, the chance that American Foul Brood can attack successfully is almost nil.

And where European Foul Brood affects the larva almost immediately after it enters its body, American Foul Brood doesn't show the effects of its attack until after the capping of the cell has taken place.

If any of the brood capping seems discolored or greasy, a beekeeper may be in for trouble. If any of the cappings are sunken, slightly concave, there is even more chance that there is trouble.

Inside the questionable cell, after the capping has been removed from it, the larva that is infected will be yellowish, and shrunken, not filling out the cell as does good healthy brood.

As the disease progresses, the larva or pupa will shrink more and more, and soften until it finally becomes a dark, shapeless mass. If you touch it with the point of a pencil it will stick to the point, draw out and string with tremendous elasticity. This sticky, elastic, rotten, moist mass is what makes American Foul Brood so hard to stamp out. European Foul Brood will be dry, and possibly granular, so that the bees can remove it and completely clean the cell ready for a new egg. But the sticky mass which results from the attack of American Foul Brood adheres to the inside of the cell wall, dries, and defies every attempt of the cleanup squad to remove it.

The result is that it is left dried and adhering to the inside wall, containing thousands of bacilli, so that the egg which is laid in that cell has absolutely no chance of escaping contagion.

This is why the only cure is ruthless destruction of infected areas of comb, or of whole frames or hives. The hive body itself must be thoroughly disinfected somehow or burned, to save the other units of the apiary.

And this isn't as easy as it sounds. Heat, boiling or some

other application of extreme heat, will destroy most bacteria. Not always the bacillus of the American Foul Brood. It sometimes forms a thickened wall around itself and has survived hours of boiling.

There are chemicals which will destroy it, but these will, for the most part, destroy too the larvae and the bees.

If a hive weakens from Foul Brood and eventually dies out and is left undestroyed, sooner or later bees from other colonies will find the hive or tree abandoned, will carry its stores home with them, and their hives in turn will be infected.

It is, as I have said, a horrible scourge in the bee world. A beekeeper who buys secondhand supplies or comb that he doesn't know all about, or who feeds unknown honey instead of sugar water, lays his colonies open to the ravages of the disease needlessly. Even if he uses tools on his other hives with which he has taken apart infected colonies, he's asking for trouble.

A strong colony will resist the disease better than a weaker one, of course. But there seems to be no difference in the susceptibility of the various races of bees to American Foul Brood as there is with the European variety. All races seem equally to succumb to it.

Only the queen grub, which is fed on royal jelly exclusively and not on honey, and some of the drone grubs which get special food above the quality of mass feeding for the larvae of the workers, will not become infected. So the queen and drones may hatch out when all but a few of the worker larvae die, and theoretically may mate and start the race again, when disease has wiped out the bees of a given area in the wild state. They must, and usually will, abandon the old home with its diseased stench, and take residence in a new home with new combs.

The help the beekeeper can give in American Foul Brood,

AFB, is mainly preventive. Here, as is the case so often with bees, keeping the colony very strong is one of the best ways to help. Then the giving of sulfathiazole, one half gram to a gallon of sugar syrup as a preventive measure, is considered worthwhile. For a while it was thought that in sulfathiazole, beekeepers had a cure for AFB. For a while good results were reported in some cases. But in most of these cases where a cure had been reported, there was a later recurrence. There is, therefore, as far as I can ascertain, no sure cure for AFB. The recurrences seemed to relegate sulfathiazole to the role of preventive insurance to keep a healthy colony healthy. In that role it seems to be outstanding.

What, then, do beekeepers do who find AFB contamination in one or more of their colonies? These colonies must be destroyed. A. I. Root says that it is better to have a government inspector do the destroying than for the colony owner to try to do it himself. The inspector has done it many times, will leave no careless or unrecognized source of reinfection open.

Briefly, the inspector will have a hole dug at least eighteen inches deep, more than big enough to handle all the infected equipment. The bees in the infected colony are gassed and killed at night when all are inside the hive. To have any left alive with infected honey in their honey stomachs is to defeat the purpose of the burning and infect some other hive. Then a fire is started in the pit and the combs, both brood and honey, are fed to this fire. All of them. Next the inside of the hive itself is burned out with gasoline.

This is the only sure way to eradicate the disease. It is like an operation for appendicitis. It is very painful to the beekeeper, and very expensive. But it is better than having the patient (in this case the whole apiary) die.

If it is done when bees are out in the field, returning bees will come to the old stand, find no hive there, and possibly be allowed to enter nearby colonies. The honey in *their* stomachs would theoretically not be from the stores of the infected hive as would be the case with bees that had escaped from a hive. It would be new honey. But still there might be some way in which those bees could carry the infection, and no such chance should be taken.

Work has been done, too, on breeding for resistance to AFB. Some colonies have seemed able to resist infection while it was all around them, and the colony was most surely exposed to it. The idea has been to breed from these hard-to-infect colonies.

Outstanding work has been done along these lines. But these efforts so far are not enough advanced so that a beekeeper can requeen with bee royalty of resistant stock, and cure an already infected colony. Even the men doing the experimental work all advise that infected colonies be burned. To make the matter of resistant-stock-success less sure, is the finding of the experimenters that bees resistant to AFB in one locality may not be, in another. This is the sort of finding that causes a conscientious scientist to snap at his wife and kids when he goes home at night.

As if these brood diseases were not enough, there are also diseases that attack the adult bees. The major ones we'll mention.

We have alluded in previous chapters to the danger of dysentery among bees. In some cases this may be an infectious disease. But in most cases it is a diarrhealike scourge. It comes from, and is aggravated by, cold, dampness, and a weak colony that cannot maintain cluster warmth. It is particularly prevalent among colonies wintered in a cellar where the temperature is allowed to go below 40 degrees and stay there for long periods. The bees cannot fly out and rid themselves of their accumulated feces, and dysentery results.

Too, if a colony is weak it must fan heavily to maintain cluster warmth. This means heavy consumption of food. And this in turn means greater feces accumulations.

So the need to void themselves comes more often to these bees. In heavily infected colonies, bees will die. This weakens the colony still further. Those left will void themselves over combs and the inside walls of the colony which further aggravates the infection. Such a colony will probably die out completely.

The cure is, of course, a strong colony and warm weather. When you have a strong colony, even one day of warm weather which allows the bees to fly out away from the hive, will make a tremendous difference. Dysentery is closely allied to "Spring Dwindling" which is also the result of a poor colony, poorly managed, with not enough stores or bees to keep a normal temperature.

Bees are, too, subject to a Bee Paralysis. It seems to be mildly contagious, especially in the South. In northern beeyards it seldom spreads. But in southern yards it sometimes affects all of the beekeeper's colonies. The bee abdomen is greatly swollen, and has a greasy look. The infected bees will crawl or be pulled to the entrance, and will crawl off, away from the hive, and die. Requeening will in most cases clear up Bee Paralysis.

Nosema appears in this country to some degree, but it is a very heavy loss factor in Europe. It comes from a single-celled protozoan parasite which is called *Nosema apis*. This attacks and breeds in the stomach of the bee. High temperatures will wipe it out. It breeds best about 88 degrees, but at the human body temperature of 98.6 or above, the disease will not develop, and those infected with it will gradually clear of it providing the temperature remains high.

Acarapis is sometimes called Isle of Wight disease. It came from the Isle of Wight to England where, at the beginning of this century, it nearly wiped out all the bees in that country. The bees' wings sometimes appear to be out of joint and they lose the use of some of their legs. This disease is caused by a small mite, *Acarapis woodi*. Ten or twelve years after Great Britain's trouble, the United States tried to find cases of Acarapsis in this country and found none. Because they found none, an embargo was placed upon the importation of all adult bees from foreign countries except Canada, unless the Secretary of Agriculture should decide that no cases of this disease had been found in that particular country.

The disease is therefore of no interest in the United States, except as something to know exists. This is a very pleasant state of affairs since we have plenty of other troubles to worry about here without taking on that one.

There is, too, a "Disappearing Disease," a symptom of which is the fact that afflicted bees run around in front of the hive like so many crickets. They seem to be very distressed. Their wings, too, seem sometimes to be out of joint. This out-of-joint symptom is like that of Acarapis, but that disease doesn't give us the cricket bit. Disappearing Disease is so named because in about ten days it disappears from the colony completely. None of the others do this automatically. Far from it. So a beekeeper smiles broadly and shakes hands with himself when it is established that Disappearing Disease and not one of the others is attacking one of his colonies.

So these are the typhoids, the chickenpoxes, the Asian flus of the bee world. The real killer is the American Foul Brood. We find that a strong Italian or Caucasian colony, with a good source of new honey to feed strong larvae, with plenty of bees to take care of the hygiene of the hive and to clean any cells that have been infected, can fight off an attack of European Foul Brood, sometimes even without the help of the beekeeper. But seldom if ever can it fight off an attack of American Foul Brood without help, because of the sticky, gummy infection, remaining in even cleaned cells, which will spread the infection to generations yet unborn, from eggs yet unlaid, until the hive becomes too weakened to fight longer. Few people outside the industry realize that these insects, whose stingers they fear so unreasoningly, in turn have their dread enemies with which they too must contend. Or that this contention is often unsuccessful, and a whole colony may perish.

II

---◆◆◆---

HONEY

Honey is the end result of apiculture. The nearly universal love of honey is what motivates all the study, experimentation, manipulation. We've seen how a bear will sit and undergo hundreds of stings on his nose and face and eyes while he yelps, but will stubbornly go on digging honey out of a hive body and eating it. And at the other end of the size scale we've watched ants wage a ruthless military campaign to get it. In between, there are insects, birds, animals and humans who are willing to pay any price for it in stings. And there are hundreds more categories of creatures who will not pay the sting price, but dearly love to eat honey when they can do so without physical danger.

What, then, is all the excitement about? Why is honey so pleasing to so many?

Well, first off it is sweet. Very sweet. And it has a distinctive flavor which runs from mild and delicate in clover, to strong and pungent in buckwheat. We humans start as children with a passion for sweets, and most of us never completely outgrow it. In other words, honey tastes delicious to us. So we want it. It's as simple as that.

To children and the majority of adults, that's all they know about it. And, for that matter, all they care. But doctors, nurses, dieticians, chemists, bakers, candy makers, have studied it and its effect on humans. And almost without exception, they give it their okay. They have discovered some very interesting things about honey that have nothing at all to do with its taste.

First, its sweetness comes from three sugars, levulose, dextrose and sucrose. These are in a water solution, along with tiny quantities of minerals, acids and protein. Honey contains about 40 percent levulose, 34 percent dextrose, 2 percent sucrose and 17 percent water. All the rest of the elements together make up the other 7 percent. There is iron, lime, sodium, sulphur, magnesium, phosphorous, pollen, manganese, aluminum, calcium, copper, albumen, dextrine, nitrogen and traces of others besides the protein and acids. It sounds impressive, but it doesn't amount to much in comparison with the sugars and the moisture.

When the nectar is gathered it varies widely in composition, and often contains more sucrose (cane sugar) than it does levulose (fruit sugar) or dextrose (grape sugar). It ends up as 2 percent, but in the beginning it may be in greater quantity than either of the other two sugars.

And in it there is an enzyme called invertase which is a catalyst that slowly changes that sucrose into the other two sugars. This change takes place in the honey stomach of the field bee, in the honey stomach of the house bee when she takes nectar from the field bee to a cell, or when she moves it from one cell to another or works it. It further occurs while the nectar is lying in the uncapped cell and moisture is being evaporated from it. Thus honey which is being ripened from such nectar, and from which excess moisture has been evaporated, gets to that 40 percent = 34 percent = 2 percent sugar ratio we spoke of above.

Honey, then, is not "made," in the sense of manufactured, by the bees, as we commonly say it is. Nectar makes *itself* into honey with its self-contained enzymes during the bees' collecting and moisture-evaporating processes.

The fact that bees do not "make" honey is dramatically proved by what happens when they are fed sugar water. They take this, treat it just as they would treat nectar, store it in cells and fan it. And when they get through they still have evaporated-down sugar water. They haven't been able to change it into honey. It is the nectar and its components that make themselves into honey, with an assist scored to the credit of the bees for proper handling.

Levulose and dextrose are called simple, or invert sugars, because when they are together produced from sucrose by invertase, they rotate polarized light to the left, whereas sucrose itself has been rotating it to the right. They invert the sugar; the process has been termed inversion.

Sounds complicated, doesn't it? And what does all this mean to you as a honey eater?

Well, levulose and dextrose, as we have said, are simple sugars. That means they go directly into your blood stream without first being digested. Thus the term "predigested" used to describe the state honey attains. Regular sugar will not do this. It must first go through a change or digestive process or be inverted before it can be used in the bloodstream.

So honey is a quick-energy food. You take it into your system and it supplies energy immediately. In the blood stream it is burned slowly, and in the process becomes carbon dioxide and water. And this burning supplies the energy for heat and muscular activity.

A lot of people for this reason, and I'm one of them, when they feel tired from a great expenditure of physical or mental energy, eat a couple of teaspoons of honey or mix the honey with a glass of hot water and drink it. If you do this, in almost all cases you will quickly lose the tired feeling. Some athletic directors and coaches give it to their charges before they compete. This is particularly true in the case of track coaches; their sport requires, in many cases, short bursts of supreme energy. Dr. Jarvis, in his long-time best-selling book *Folk Medicine* recommends that vinegar be added to the honey and water.

In the matter of caloric energy, honey, a tablespoon of which contains 100 calories, outdistances any other type of sweet. For instance, it takes 1¾ tablespoons of corn syrup, 1½ of maple syrup, 4 of maple sugar, 2 of white granulated, 2 of brown sugar, to produce the same caloric energy.

And it far outdistances most other foods. There is more than seven times as much caloric energy in a pound of honey as in a pound of apples, carrots or tomatoes, and more than twice as much as in eggs (624 as against 1,540).

Being made up of invert simple sugars, honey needs no digestion by invalids with stomach problems, or by older people whose digestive systems are causing trouble.

Those minute quantities of acid (0.1 percent) in honey are malic and citric acids. Malic acid is found in apples and some other fruits; citric acid is found in all citrus fruits.

I mention this because for years honey was thought to contain formic acid. There have been many misconceptions about bees and honey over the centuries (like that matter of their springing from a dead ox) but that formic acid bit must be considered a strong contender for the prize.

According to this theory bees were supposed to be working masons. They were supposed to use their stingers as trowels in capping honey cells. The mental picture of a bee looking back over her shoulder while she troweled the wax of a capping, is an intriguing one. When she was through she was supposed to jab this trowel of hers through the capping and into the honey, and inject venom into it which was supposed to be mostly formic acid.

This isn't even good craftsmanship. No union boss anywhere would let you jab your trowel through your work when it was completed. And it had a lot more than this against it as a principle of bee behavior. Venom isn't made up of formic acid, as we'll see in a later chapter. And the bee stinger with its microscopic barbs has no flat trowel side.

But ignoring these things, the main fault to be found with the theory was that it just wasn't true. Bees don't do it and never did. They do drag their abdomens close to the surface they are working on, and this was probably what started the idea. The theory was primarily responsible for the idea that honey contains formic acid. It just doesn't.

With any popular food product there will always be detractors and there will always be adulterators. Adulteration of honey is punishable by a heavy fine.

Simple adulteration, the adding of sugar water or plain sucrose soluton to honey, is luckily very easy to detect. Honey turns light rays that have passed through polarization, to the left. (To be sure, dextrose does turn light rays to the right, but there is always less dextrose than levulose in honey, and levulose turns polarized rays of light to the left.) So honey turns this light to the left, also.

When cane sugar or glucose is added in an adulterating quantity, the polarized light is turned to the right. The inspector who finds honey that turns polarized light rays to the right knows he has a case of adulteration on his hands.

Knowing this, adulterators either don't adulterate any

more, or they do it more cleverly. Instead of a plain sugar-water solution, they add commercial invert sugar. This is much harder to detect, but it can be done.

The commercial invert sugar is made by treating cane sugar with an acid. However, this allows inspectors to use the resorcinol test. This test will, if there is acid in the honey in quantity great enough to have changed cane sugar to invert sugar, turn the honey red. Ordinary honey that doesn't contain inverting acid, will not turn red under the resorcinol test.

Another test is to isolate from the honey the acid that inverted the cane sugar. If it isn't an acid that's supposed to be in honey, or is in too heavy quantity, your honey has been adulterated.

One kind of honey that nobody has yet been able successfully to adulterate, is comb honey. The task of trying to adulterate each separate capped cell would make almost any criminal throw up his hands in horror and accept honest employment. It would be less work.

As for honey's detractors, they have, like detractors of most other products, been mainly people interested in selling a rival product. Mostly in one way or another, it has taken the form of viewing with extreme alarm the granulation of honey.

Granulation is a fact of life in apiary work. But in spite of all rumors to the contrary, granulation does not spoil honey. Nor does it indicate adulteration as many people firmly believe.

To oversimplify, honey granulates because it is a supersaturated solution of sugars. You can dissolve far more sugar in water at high temperatures than at low. Then in the process of curing honey as we have seen, you evaporate water from this solution. Later when winter comes, the temperature of the solution is lowered. When you remove water and lower the temperature the solution goes from saturated to supersaturated.

The sugar remains in supersaturated solution for a while, but if it is subjected to too much of this evaporating and temperature-lowering treatment it will go back to being a solid. It will, in other words, crystallize.

This is the general principle; there are some interesting ways in which the general behavior pattern may be retarded or altered. To begin with, some honeys crystallize quicker than others. Alfalfa honey will crystallize or granulate far, far faster than will tupelo honey. This is because the dextrose, which goes to saturation much quicker than levulose, and is therefore the sugar that is crystallizing, comes much closer to equaling the levulose percentagewise in alfalfa than it does in tupelo. Therefore it is in greater supersaturation; therefore crystals form quicker.

Temperature makes a big difference, too. But, just as high temperatures retard crystallization, lower temperatures retard it, too, strange as that may seem. Fifty degrees will bring on crystallization the fastest. Down to that point crystallization increases with each degree the temperature drops. Below that, it decreases.

This is because at temperatures lower than that, honey thickens and its viscosity increases. This retards the liquid solution in reaching the crystals already formed. And reaching crystals already formed is what causes a supersaturation to further crystallize.

This is, too, the reason stirring will crystallize honey faster than allowing it to stand still. Stirring brings the solution to the surfaces of the crystals already formed much faster, so it crystallizes faster.

Again, when small crystals and large crystals in equal

amounts and weights are present in two samples of honey, the small crystals will cause their particular sample to crystallize much faster than the large crystals will granulate theirs. There is less surface exposed in a large crystal than there is in the same weight of small crystals. So crystallization goes on faster.

Theoretically, if all crystals, no matter how minute, could be removed from a given batch of honey there would be no crystallization of that honey. But no matter how fine the filter, this just can't be done. Conversely, you can dump fine crystals into a batch of honey and then stir and make it crystallize at a tremendous rate. This is the way honey is changed into a very tasty creamed honey spread, by breaking up the crystals by beating; this exposes lots more surfaces. The same beating brings a lot of solution against those surfaces to give you your smooth honey spread.

This creamed honey can be made commercially by the Dyce process or the New Zealand process, both of which "seed" honey with fine-crystal granulated honey at just over room temperatures after the honey has been heated to remove yeasts and large crystals. After the seeding the honey is placed in containers and left at temperatures of around 57 degrees. The crystallization of the honey will become complete and give a fine cream honey in about four days.

To return granulated honey to a liquid, heat it to a temperature much below boiling, and leave it there a long time until its crystals seem completely to be dissolved. Honey will take less harm if heated in the top of a double boiler, the bottom of which holds hot water, than it will if its dish is exposed to direct heat. Buckwheat honey must be heated with greater care than other honeys because heat harms it quicker.

Another favorite tongue-clicker among honey detractors

is the theory that being so sweet, honey must carry and breed bacteria in incredible quantities. It furnishes them a perfect place for breeding or dividing, or whatever method that particular set of bacteria have chosen to get the propagation job done. If, people whisper, milk carries and breeds the germs of typhoid fever, just think what honey could do.

Dr. W. G. Sackett, a bacteriologist, thought this sounded reasonable and he set out to prove it. He introduced the germs of various diseases into batches of honey. Then he ran a series of tests on these.

All the typhoid fever germs were gone in 48 hours. The germs of dysentery were all dead in 10 hours. He obtained like results with the other germs he had used.

Over and over honey has proved to be antiseptic, a killer of germs, and not a carrier. This is because honey's acidity and density are very rough on the poor working bacterium. The reason AFB can live in honey is that it is spore-forming. These spores lie dormant in honey. However, AFB will not attack humans, and most bacteria harmful to us do not form spores.

We have seen that honey has only about 7 percent of variable elements. One of the incredible truths of the bee world, then, is that the product of these tiny creatures can vary so in color and taste from one area and time to another, with so small a percentage variable.

The variations stem from the differences in the nectar which each flower produces. Remember, a bee will usually stick to one species of flower when collecting a load of nectar. It will usually pick the most abundant flower of the area and time, because if there are a lot of these flowers, moving from one to another wastes less time. When you consider that other bees will probably pick that same flower for that same reason, you can see why the area of comb that the bees are working at any given time will have mostly honey from the same flower species. The more of those flowers there are, the more the honey will be from those particular flowers.

The difference between the honey produced from two different flowers can be spectacular. The difference between buckwheat honey and clover honey is nearly as great as the difference between clover honey and maple syrup.

Honey can be so light-colored that it is called "water-white." This is an exaggeration of course, but it gives you the idea. Then there is amber honey, and dark-colored honey which is dark brownish. There are all sorts of variations within these main categories.

In light-colored honeys, clover honey is the ultimate. It is delicate in flavor and texture, completely delicious. It is produced from all the clovers: white, red, sweet, mammoth and alsike.

Other water-white honeys vary little in color from it. They include alfalfa, basswood (a tall-tree honey) apple, bean, cotton, orange, palmetto, tupelo (another tall-tree honey) and mangrove. In the West there are mesquite and sage. In Europe there's sainfoin, and in the tropics there are logwood, campeche and campanilla. There are a lot of other, lesser light-colored honeys, too.

It's even possible for a honey to be light in one place and amber in another, the difference obviously tied in with the temperature and soil differences of the two locations. Alfalfa is a prime example. It is light colored in New England, but amber in California and Arizona. It tastes different there, too. In Australia eucalyptus honey is prized, but honey from the same tree in California is considered to be nowhere near as tasty.

In the amber category the best-known honey is goldenrod. There are also the tree honeys, magnolia, eucalyptus, poplar, sumac. And in tropical areas the royal palm, a huge palm tree that looks as if it had a poured-cement trunk.

In the dark-honey category, by far the best known is buckwheat honey. It is grown both in the United States and Europe. Russia used to produce a tremendous crop of buckwheat honey. If you can believe what they say, they still do. New York and Pennsylvania produce more buckwheat honey than any other area in our country. In New York there's almost always a good crop of buckwheat nectar harvested no matter what the conditions. But in nearby Ohio, sometimes the plants produce little or no nectar. Buckwheat is a flower that farmer-beekeepers often plant to give them a money crop and give their bees a fine field in which to work. Buckwheat will actually stay in bloom for thirty to thirty-five days, which gives the bees a long crack at it after the clover flow is over. Some farmers even furnish free buckwheat seed the first year to any of their neighbors who will plant it each year.

In areas where a lot of buckwheat is grown, people love the taste of buckwheat honey. It is very strong. In areas where it is not grown, it has little market. People have not acquired a taste for it. In France there is one kind of commercial bread baked with buckwheat honey. Producers of other dark honeys have tried to get the bakers to substitute some other kind. The bakers mostly remain unconvinced and stick to their buckwheat.

A dark honey that we don't produce, but that is a big item in the European economy, is heather honey. This is strong-flavored honey, so thick that very often the extractor cannot be used to remove it from the combs. In some parts of Europe it is gathered on a two-crop basis; the bees work on clover during the summer, and then are moved to the heaths. Here again there is a difference in the quality of honey in different areas. Scotch heather honey brings a high price, but English heather honey sells for much less. Here, though, the difference stems from a different species of heather grown in each of these two localities.

Honey is known to most people as a table delicacy and spread. What they seldom realize is that honey is used in many commercial preparations, and in many ways.

By far the greatest use by volume of honey is in cooking, mostly in baking. And this use is to a very great extent the result of its hygroscopic properties. In less fancy words, it absorbs and retains moisture.

In baking, this keeps the product moist much longer than does sweetening it with plain sugar. Bread or cookies baked with honey will remain soft and moist and pliable long after bread or cookies made from the same recipe, but with all-sugar sweetening, have grown hard and dry.

Honey can be used in home canning, in the making of ice cream, but its hygroscopic properties in most cases work against its use in candy making. In World War I when sugar was so scarce, honey was used in making soft drinks. It is not particularly good for carbonated drinks because it makes them cloudy. But this of course does no harm in cola drinks.

Honey can be worked into soft butter, about 30 per cent honey if your family is high on sweets, and less if it isn't. The resulting spread must be kept in the refrigerator just as you would keep any butter. Prof. P. H. Tracy, while he was with the dairy department of the University of Illinois, described a method for combining dairy cream with honey. He takes a cream with 75 percent butterfat content, and mixes it with a mild honey in the ratio of 42 percent honey and 58 percent cream.

When it hardens in the container this mixture must be refrigerated and treated as butter. Some baby doctors have recommended adding prescribed amounts of honey to infant formulas. In most cases the babies recommend it, too, after the first try.

And now comes the amazing use; honey in cosmetics. It is used with a variety of other ingredients in various formulas for skin creams or face packs. Mostly these packs (or even extracted honeys without being mixed with anything) are left on the face for half an hour, then removed with a cloth and warm water. (Probably makes kissing an extra delight.) Then an astringent is applied to the face. Honey is used with oil of sweet almonds as a hand lotion. And in the days when women worried about freckles instead of trying to make them into one large, overlapping freckle, there was a composition of honey, glycerine, citric acid and alcohol to remove those freckles. Honey has, at various times by various people, been mixed with soap.

This use as a cosmetic base probably stems from the antiseptic powers of honey mentioned above. Dr. Bodag Beck, in his writings, says that honey placed on ulcerated areas or on wounds will cause great quantities of lymph to flow and will flush the wound, cleanse it and promote healing. The use of honey in this way was a home remedy in remote areas of Europe and of our country before modern transportation made doctors and hospitals more readily available. In the same way, honey has been used to keep the air away from burned areas of the human skin. Here again that same antiseptic quality comes to the fore.

Dr. Jarvis in *Folk Medicine* says that honey and vinegar will cure many ills and guard against many others. And that the chewing of honey cappings will have a marked effect for the better on sinus disorders. Obviously many people must have thought they were helped by his suggestions, or those who tried those remedies would have deadened the sale of the book instead of promoting it further until it became one of the greatest best sellers of recent times. The American Medical Association, however, has been considerably less than enthusiastic about these matters all the way through.

Dr. Jarvis recommends drinking honey and vinegar when you have a cold. And another folk remedy has it that the juice of a lemon and a tablespoon of honey mixed into a glass of hot water, if taken twice a day, also will help fight this disease.

Roughly 25 percent of the honey produced in the United States each year is used by bakers. This is an astonishing total. The two main products are bread and cake.

Bread is an easier bakery product to produce with honey than cake. The start of its popularity coincided with the ascendancy of whole wheat bread. Honey gave the bread a special aroma and made a small difference in flavor. But most important of all was that hygroscopic, moisture-absorbing quality which the baking industry hadn't previously realized honey possessed. This, as we have seen, would keep the bread soft and fresh much longer than the industry had been able to keep fresh any of its bread sweetened with only sugar. It was soon found, too, that honey provided an even better food for the yeast than sugar, and gave the bread a beautiful brown-colored crust because it caramelized under heat.

It was in the early 1930's that the baking industry began to take advantage of this discovery to any marked degree. Bakers made their bread with, on the average, 6 percent liquid honey content and they called it "honey bread."

By 1941 the Food and Drug Administration got into the act to protect, as they put it, the public. They said that nothing which was used in only a 6 percent quantity should be allowed to give its name to the end product. To call a bread with only 6 percent honey in it, "honey bread" was misleading the public. They drew up a tentative decree that in order to use the term "honey bread," a baker had to put 20 percent honey in it.

This was like decreeing that to label biscuits as "baking powder biscuits," over three times as much baking powder as the recipe called for must be used. And any cook knows what would happen if you tried to do that.

Protests came in from consumers, bakers, beemen, and storekeepers. A hearing was held and all concerned testified that this was absurd. You'd have a product that was too sweet, far too soggy, and with a synthetic rubber crust that would have been the envy of the Goodyear people. The commercial bakers added that it would be extremely hard for their mechanical mixing machines to work the dough, and unless they were able to buy the very lightest of honeys, would give the product an unpleasant flavor that would keep housewives away from it in great droves.

The Food and Drug Administration kept the industry on the hot seat for two years in this matter before they published a report outlining their demands for a 20 percent content of liquid honey, and the baking industry's suggested lawful minimum of 4 percent, and saying that there seemed to be "no demand for bread and rolls containing the proportion of honey proposed by the F.D.A. The evidence does not establish that such a proposed definition and standard of identity would be reasonable." Since they knew it didn't two years before, when the testimony was taken, it seemed to the bee and baking industries that they were being a bit tardy and ungracious in their admission that they had been wrong.

Honey cake is a much more difficult proposition. In my wife's recipe file, placed there during World War II when sugar was scarce, is a card labeled "Facts in Making Cakes with Honey."

Among the suggestions listed are:

Successful cakes depend on tested recipes, level accurate measurements and standard measuring spoons, correct baking temperatures and a well-used oven.

Use light honey (light in color and mild in flavor).

Always be sure to *cream* shortening, add honey, cream again. If honey and shortening are not creamed well, cakes will have a shaded appearance.

Be sure the shortening is soft, especially if an electric mixer is not available.

Add sifted dry ingredients alternately with milk, starting with dry ingredients and ending with same.

Honey cakes require more salt than ordinary sugar cakes.

Bake in 350 degree oven the same as you would an all-sugar cake.

Rap the pan two or three times on the bottom after the batter is put in to take out the larger air bubbles.

Honey cakes may be kept for some time and still be moist.

The Division of Home Economics of the University of California at Davis worked out a formula for substituting honey for sugar in any standard white-cake recipe; 3/4 cup of honey to replace 1 cup of sugar. And at the same time decrease the amount of milk by 3 1/3 teaspoons. (This is to make up for the 17 percent water which we have already learned that honey contains.)

I've talked to fine cooks and bakers who substitute cup for cup, and do not decrease milk content. They claim that to decrease the milk causes the cake to crumble. Certainly no more than the 17 percent moisture should be removed.

The University of California people at Davis came to the conclusion that between 25 percent and 50 percent of the called-for sweetening should be honey. More than 50 percent meant adding extra soda to neutralize the honey's natural acids; otherwise you'd get a heavy, soggy, strong-tasting cake. And they proved with their experiments that honey cake will be moister on the third day than on the day it was baked.

Here are a few representative recipes:

WHOLE WHEAT HONEY BREAD

1½ cups potato water   2 cakes (or 2 envelopes) yeast
⅔ cup cooking oil   4 cups white flour, sifted
¾ cup honey   4 cups whole wheat flour
1½ teaspoons salt   1 cup bran
1½ cups lukewarm water

Put one medium-sized potato and its cooking water through a sieve to get a total of 1½ cups. Add the cooking oil, salt and honey to the hot potato water. When this becomes lukewarm, add the yeast which you have softened in the 1½ cups lukewarm water. Stir carefully and at length. Combine the flours and the bran in a pan and stir the potato mixture into this. Again mix at length. Knead until elastic and smooth. Place in a greased bowl, cover and let rise until you have twice the amount you started with. Form into loaves, place in greased tins. Allow to rise again until double in bulk. Bake in a 350-degree oven for one hour. Take the bread out of the pans at once and place on a wire rack to cool.

Unlike most homemade bread, this bread toasts beautifully.

HONEY LAYER CAKE

½ cup honey   ½ cup milk
½ cup shortening   2 cups flour
½ cup sugar   3 teaspoons baking powder
2 eggs beaten   ¼ teaspoon salt
            2 teaspoons cream

Cream the shortening, honey, sugar. Add the beaten eggs and milk to the sifted dry ingredients, first a little of one, then a little of the other. Add the cream and stir a little but don't beat. Bake in two shallow pans in a 350 degree oven until brown.

And a *Honey Icing* for this cake:

Boil one cup of honey one minute. Beat two egg whites and add the honey slowly, beating until the whole is stiff enough to hold its shape. The honey will cause the icing to take on moisture, so it must be eaten immediately and not kept as other icings are.

HONEY CHOCOLATE CAKE

3 squares unsweetened chocolate	2 unbeaten eggs
2/3 cup honey	1¾ cups sifted cake flour
½ cup shortening	¾ teaspoon salt
½ cup sugar	1 teaspoon soda
1 teaspoon vanilla	2/3 cup water

Melt the chocolate over hot but not boiling water. Add the honey and blend. Allow these ingredients to cool until lukewarm. Cream the shortening and add the sugar slowly. Keep on creaming until light and fluffy. Add the lukewarm mixture you first made, and the vanilla. Blend. Add the eggs, one at a time, beating well between. Add salt and soda to the flour, then sift three times. Add the dry ingredients alternately with water, a small amount at a time, beginning and ending with flour; beat well after each addition. Pour batter into greased layer pans and bake in a 350 degree oven for 30 to 35 minutes. Cool.

HONEY DATE SANDWICH COOKIES

Filling

½ pound raisins	1 cup honey
½ pound dates	1 cup boiling water

Combine these four ingredients in a saucepan and cook until thick. Cool.

COOKIE DOUGH

1¾ cups quick-cooking oat-
 meal
1½ cups flour
1 cup brown sugar
1 teaspoon baking powder
1 teaspoon salt
¾ cup shortening

Mix the dry ingredients, cut in the shortening and mix thoroughly as for pie dough. Spread half the mixture on a greased cookie sheet, spread the filling over this, then over this spread the other half of the dough. Bake twenty to twenty-five minutes in a moderate oven and cut in squares.

CHOCOLATE CHIP COOKIES

½ cup butter
½ cup honey
1 small egg
1 cup sifted flour
1 teaspoon baking powder
¼ teaspoon salt
½ teaspoon vanilla
½ cup semi-sweet chocolate
 chips
¼ cup nutmeats, chopped

Cream honey and butter until light and fluffy. Add egg and beat well. Sift flour, baking powder and salt twice. Add flour mixture to butter mixture; then add vanilla and blend well. Fold in chocolate chips and nuts. Chill and drop by teaspoonfuls on greased cookie sheet. Bake at 375 degrees for 12 minutes.

As we mentioned, the hygroscopic properties of honey make it a poor bet in most candy recipes, except where caramelization is expected. But here is a fudge recipe that I like.

HONEY CHOCOLATE FUDGE

⅔ cup honey   ⅛ teaspoon salt
2 cups sugar   1 teaspoon vanilla
¾ cup cream   ½ cup chopped nutmeats.
1 square unsweetened choco-
    late

Add the honey and the cream and the chocolate to the sugar. Mix. Cook slowly over low heat until no grains of sugar remain on back of spoon. Turn up flame and cook until drops will form a ball in cold water. Remove from fire, add salt and vanilla and beat about 20 minutes till mixture has lost its gloss. Add nutmeats and pour into buttered pan. When almost cold mark into squares.

My wife, possibly in deference to my feelings about bees and honey, makes a honey dressing for salads that I like on fruit salads. She takes a standard French Dressing recipe, makes it with lemon juice instead of vinegar, and adds one tablespoon of honey.

The Honey Grapefruit she serves, I like very much. Especially I like it if we've happened to be stuck with a very sour batch of grapefruit. She halves them, cuts out the center, which leaves a round hole. This she fills with honey and lets some flow out onto the surface of the grapefruit half. The grapefruit is then allowed to stand a short time before serving, to let the honey mix with the juice.

Part of the fun of cooking with honey is that you can get a couple of hundred different flavor gradations all out of the same recipe, each time you use honey from a different nectar source. The cake made with clover honey, for instance, will have a slightly different flavor and sometimes even a different aroma, from one which you made with orange blossom honey. And cooking with honey makes the whole house smell fantastically wonderful.

So we find that honey is a delicious spread. It is predigested, so that it goes at once into the bloodstream to add energy. It can be used in cooking, and gathers moisture to any product into which it is baked, thus keeping that product fresh and moist. It is antiseptic. It is used in cosmetics, and some people, even doctors, attribute disease preventive and even curative properties to it in certain situations.

Maybe all of us would use it because of its fine characteristics even if it tasted worse than some horrible headshaking medicine. Its delicious taste is just a delightful bonus.

12

---◆◆---

GENERAL APICULTURE

Man has had very little success in changing the Rock of Gibraltar. He's tunneled into it, added electric lights and gun emplacements. But he hasn't moved it, or turned it, or changed its basic appearance. He hasn't even, in spite of pictorial evidence to the contrary, printed the word PRUDENTIAL across the front of it.

Man has had the same resounding failure when it comes to changing the habits of honeybees. Some of those habits make him swear constantly. He would change them at once if he could. The swarming instinct, the gluing everything with propolis, the inability to fight AFB, are three of these. And probably not even the greatest of them. From his point of view, other habits could hardly be improved upon. The selfless working herself to death, the flying in a straight line to the colony when full, the storing of surplus honey away from the pollen and brood so he can rob the colony better, are such habits.

There are still other habits, like the ability to sting, which the beekeeper would like to change one minute—when he's being set upon by a "hot" colony—and which he blesses the next when he sees a neighbor's boy in the moonlight, bent on free honey, running empty-handed across a field, with a cloud of bees around his head.

Good bad or indifferent, they've all been the same as far as any change goes. There just hasn't been any. Bees right now try to behave exactly the way they tried to behave two or three thousand years ago or more, and during all the years in between.

The only thing left for man, then, has been to learn as much as he could about those behavior habits and the reasons for them, and then try to harness them to his advantage. Or at least to figure up some way to negate them. For instance, bees built combs of a set width, with a thicker wax rib in the center. Man devised movable frames, manufactured the thick center rib so that the cells would be the size *he* wanted them, and the bees built their combs in those frames. If you can't lick 'em, join 'em.

And all this learning about behavior habits, this experimentation to harness those habits, this systematic robbing of the surplus—millions of tons of it—is called apiculture.

Man has been diabolically ingenious in apiculture over the years. And the fact that he could write and publish a finding, or describe some outstanding success for all other beekeepers to read about and adapt to their own apiary work, has given him a tremendous advantage. New successes and new discoveries in all fields stem from the ones previously made public.

So let us examine the hive, the colony life in it, the robing, and the resulting processing and sale of the product taken from the bees. Let us do so this time not from the bees' point of view, but from the beekeeper's. To do this we'll talk about what the beekeeper would have to own and what he would have to do if he intended to keep bees commercially.

In the first place—mildly axiomatic—he would need bees. And just as important, he would need housing for them. Actually the housing should come along with the bees, or should be purchased or otherwise come by before they are.

The easiest way to start is to buy out somebody's going apiary. The price will depend on how badly the owner wants to sell and how much extra equipment is included. But to figure less than $20 to $30 per colony is unrealistic for a healthy apiary.

If it isn't healthy, in the sense of disease-free, it's like throwing dollar bills onto a fire. The cautious purchaser will have the colonies inspected by whatever agency in the government of his particular state handles bee matters before he pays. In some states an apiary could not be purchased and moved to a new location without such an inspection. Besides looking for disease, the size of the cells in the brood area must be checked. If most of these aren't worker size, the colony is a poor buy.

This method of acquisition has a lot to recommend it, and this is especially true in the case of a beekeeper new to the business. He has a chance to see how everything operates; all he must do is keep it operating that way. The things he doesn't yet know aren't so likely to ruin him. He'll probably take in a fine crop the first year.

But there are many beekeepers who have started on a shoestring. One in particular I know about was a contractor looking for a hobby. His plumber said he was having trouble at home with a swarm of bees in a wall and would probably have to pay to have them exterminated because his wife was frightened to death of them.

The contractor on the spur of the moment said he would

get rid of the bees. He bought a hive (an extremely dangerous proceeding unless that too is inspected for AFB), borrowed a bee veil, hived the swarm and took it home in the back of his car. He had some trouble because there was a hole in the hive, and the car trunk was pretty well filled with bees. But he plugged the hole, got the bees home, and had a working colony. He then advertised that he would rid anyone of bees that were annoying, and several phone calls brought him other colonies. He divided his colonies in the spring, and now has eighty colonies, and a hobby that he considers perfect for him. For one thing, while most hobbies are expensive, this one brings him an income.

In addition to hiving wild swarms, our beekeeper could hunt bees, find bee trees, and take them up. In any hiving of a wild swarm, the beeman puts frames with starter in the hive he uses, not frames with drawn-out comb. The bees will have honey in their honey stomachs. There is a possibility this honey could be contaminated with AFB. If they have no cells in the new hive to store the honey in, they will use it in manufacturing wax and drawing comb to make new cells. By the time the cells are ready and the field bees go out, the old honey will have been used up and the honey coming into the cells will have an excellent chance of being disease free. Just another of the bee habits which man has learned to turn to his advantage.

If the bees have been away from their hives for several days, the honey supplies in their honey stomachs will be used up just in eating. They will be irritable and will sting without too much provocation. Beemen are extremely careful of such swarms.

If the apiary owner doesn't want to wait for wild bees, and with them increase his holdings, he can buy package bees from the south in a three-pound package with queen. This package would contain somewhere in the neighborhood of 10,500 individual bees, which would be about 20 percent of the individuals needed for an average colony. Package bees can be installed on comb, with honey stores, since they are disease free when shipped. If they are installed in this way, and early enough to produce several cycles of brood on dandelions and fruit blossoms, they will be at full strength by clover time and probably store a fine surplus for their owner even that first year. These packages should be installed in the evening, a time when there will be less flight and less loss. They should be fed before they are installed.

My advice is to buy Italian bees, unless the apiary is in an area which has Caucasian bee apiaries all around it. Over 90 percent of the commercial bees in the United States are Italians. We've mentioned their characteristics. So you are likely to have predominantly Italian drones in the area. If you try Caucasian or some other species of bee, unless your apiary is very large, your drones will be competing with Italian drones at mating time. You'll be far less sure of getting a clear strain of bees, for that reason, than you would if you had Italian queens with mostly Italian drones around at mating time. Charles Mraz (whose apiary is pictured in this book) uses Caucasians, but he has a tremendous operation, and furnishes his own drones.

There are three ways of getting the hives in which to house swarms or package bees. You can buy them secondhand, buy them new (knocked down for shipment), or you can make them yourself.

Secondhand hives will be cheapest if the buyer can be sure of their AFB disease history. He can also make hives himself cheaper than he can buy new ones. But unless he is pretty good at carpentry, has good tools, and in addition knows exactly what he is doing, he had best disregard this possible saving and stick to the commercial product.

There are quite a few bee supply houses that will ship him knocked-down hives. The best known is the A. I. Root Company, of Medina, Ohio. Others among the better known are Dadant and Sons, Hamilton, Ohio; Walter T. Kelley Company, Clarkson, Kentucky; A. G. Woodman Company, Grand Rapids, Michigan. These companies and others print catalogs which they will send a prospective buyer on request.

Two monthly magazines, *Gleanings in Bee Culture* and *American Bee Journal,* run advertisements of firms that sell package bees with queens. These magazines, incidentally, have been publishing since 1873 and 1860 respectively.

Whether a beekeeper buys or makes his hives, they should be standard size. We've told you why the Langstroth hive became standard and is now used by some 95 percent of commercial beekeepers. If the beekeeper buys Langstroth hives, or builds them, he is therefore insuring himself a better resale price when the time comes that he wants to sell. If he himself wants to buy more equipment, he won't have to look for odd sizes, either. Almost anything he buys from anyone will fit what he already has.

Another plus for a standard hive is the fact that the beekeeper will then be using standard frames. And if his operation becomes at all extensive, there will be many times when he will want to swap frames of honey, or brood, or empty comb, from one hive to another. He won't have to worry about getting each frame back into some certain hive. His frames will be interchangeable.

Now we've got him hives, bees and frames. If he has a big operation—more than twenty or thirty hives—he will need outyard locations because an area with a two-mile radius will normally handle only about thirty colonies. The outyard sites must be picked with the same care with regard to sun, shade, windbreaks and neighbors that his main location is picked. And especially he must have planned access to it in wet weather. Above all, he must make sure that nearby there are sources of early nectar for brood rearing. He must be even surer of a nearby main honeyflow.

If he has outyards he'll need a truck. Any truck in which he plans to carry supers from the outyard (or yards) to the honey house can be smaller than the truck he would need if he were planning to move his yards from place to place for migratory beekeeping. A truck for this purpose should have a specially constructed stake body with side access, perfectly measured so that a certain number of hives exactly can be set side by side in each row so that the load will not shuck in transit. Mr. Mraz's truck has the Vermont license plate BEES.

The bigger the operation, the more the need for a honey house planned with extreme care. For a few hives or just a small yard, the owner can get by with a small shed. But the bigger the operation, the bigger the honey house. A really large one should be at least two stories, to take advantage of gravity in flowing honey from one process to another.

There is probably nothing in the bee world more astonishing in its way, than the inside of a huge honey house. It is a factory. There are vats and tanks and pipes and machines whirring. There may be a room kept at 90 degrees, possibly even made dustproof, for straining honey. There are storage areas piled high with materials—stacks of paper cartons in flat form, labels of different sizes and other paper goods—in one place. There are supplies of cans and jars, and starter sheets, and stored frames, and molds of wax. There is a loading platform exactly flush with the truck floor and the floor inside. It is made of cement, and slanted very slightly to a drain so that, unlike a wooden floor, honey drops can be flushed away completely and there will be no honey-filled cracks and fermentation.

It's a far cry, this, from that man who bought one hive and took up his plumber's problem swarm. But men have started with little and come to this many times. And all the while you watch the bustle of supers being moved, or gadgets turning and scraping and whirling. And you can't help remembering that all this began with just one tiny insect bringing one tiny drop of nectar back to her hive. The contrast is completely incongruous.

The process starts with the entrance of a super of filled capped combs. Its combs are taken out, scraped clean, and uncapped. This can be done in a number of ways, ranging from a cold uncapping knife, with an offset handle, to an electrically heated knife, thermostatically controlled. In larger operations there are even steam knives, and uncapping planes, and power uncappers.

In a really huge setup the combs may be fed between two heated, vibrating knives. The cappings fall into a "whirl-dry" which is run slowly while the uncapping process is going on, for even distribution, then run very rapidly to dry the wax and run off the previously adhering honey.

While this is going on, the uncapped combs are carried by an endless belt to the extractors. We've told you that an extractor, whirling the combs very rapidly, uses centrifugal force to draw the honey from the combs against the sides of the round extractor tank. Honey is viscous and even when it is uncapped it will not flow out much until it is forced out.

The extractors can be the hand-turned, two-frame type, for a tiny operation. Or they can be any size between it and the fifty-frame extractor into which commercial operators sometimes load as many as eighty frames. In the little extractors, the frames must be reversed by hand to whirl the honey from the second side. In the big ones the frames reverse automatically.

One big honey cooperative has four huge stainless-steel extractors hooked up in tandem and all flowing out a single pipe. The gates which let out the honey should be made of some metal besides cast iron. The acid in honey reacts with iron and has a tendency to turn the honey black when it stands against that metal too long.

From the extractor the honey goes to a straining process. This is important because honey which is heated while impurities are still in it, will have its flavor harmed. And it must later be heated before it is packaged.

Straining works best in that heated room. The honey flows, or is pumped (depending on how ingenious the architect has been) through a baffle tank or tanks which rid it of larger impurities. Then it continues through an O.A.C. strainer (Ontario Agricultural College, the developer) which passes it through smaller and smaller mesh screen starting at 12 mesh, with the last screen 80 mesh. This should give Grade A honey. Smaller operators use a series of cans instead of baffle tanks, and use a silk stocking for a strainer.

The honey is then either packed in small, fancy packs for retailing, or in bulk. If it is packed for retailing, the honey is first heated to 130 degrees to destroy yeasts and to get rid of as many of those tiny granules as possible. This will inhibit quick granulation. Under ordinary conditions, treated this way, honey can remain as much as three months on a grocery shelf without granulating.

The packs can have interesting shapes and bright, colorful labels to promote buyer interest. Five-pound tins with bigger, even more colorful labels also sell well in certain sections of the country. People will buy these from a roadside stand where they can see hives in the background, when they won't from the shelf of a store. The label usually gives the name of the flower which lent its flavor to the product (though with huge apiaries and huge vats, at best it is going to be a blend), and in many cases it also tells the housewife what to do if the honey does granulate. The labels of the larger packs may have recipes and a small dissertation on honey and its characteristics and food value. One Florida producer puts a synthetic orange blossom inside the jar, in the honey, and it causes a lot of comment.

If the honey is to be packed in bulk it probably won't be heated. The bulk pack consists of 60-pound cans or 700-pound drums. The 60-pound pack once was standard, but during World War II, to save metal, many of the larger producers went to the drums, which could be used over and over.

But a beekeeper who uses the drums must provide himself with some method of moving them from place to place, and even lifting them one atop another for storage. Usually the honey house owner installs a traveling hoist with overhead track to the storage area and loading platform, or he uses one of the new lift trucks with heavy steel fingers on the front with which he can lift the drums higher than his head, or simply lift them inches off the floor and scoot them to some other area of the honey house.

After the honey has been whirled from the combs by the centrifugal force of the extractor, the combs must be stored. They are usually stored in the supers, in a very tight room. But no matter how tight it is, wax moths will get in. The eggs come in on the frames, or on the outside of the supers, or in any one of dozens of other ways.

It is best not to store them "wet"—that is, with what adhering honey the extractor has left in them. The reason for this is that when thus stored, the minute amount of remaining honey will granulate, and the next year when these combs are refilled, these granules seed the new honey and make it granulate rapidly. In some nothern areas, the combs are piled in an isolated place, and the bees are allowed to rob them out and thus dry them completely. But there is the danger of transmitting AFB in this manner, and at least one state has a law against the practice. A small operator can place the supers back atop the hive from which they came, with an excluder, and within a day or two they will be dried out by the bees completely and can again be removed and stored.

After all the combs have been stored, chemical fumes from calcium cyanide, carbon disulphide, methyl bromide or para-dichlorobenzene are used to kill the moths. The methyl bromide will even kill the eggs. But with all of these, great care must be taken not to breathe any of the gas as it is deadly poison. This fumigation must be carried on in a regular schedule throughout the storage period to be effective. The combs should be aired when taken from such storage and before they are placed on a colony.

Usually a beekeeper maintains a wax vat, for pieces of old comb, scrapings and the like. The dried cappings and the contents of this vat are melted up, and impurities removed as much as possible, and the wax drawn off into molds. The resulting cakes are sold.

Here again propolis is the bane of the beekeepers' existence. The bees coat the inside of cells, especially when they aren't going to be used right away, with propolis to sterilize and protect them. The bees also sometimes coat the cappings of honey cells.

When the beekeeper melts down his extra wax and it turns out to be darker than it should be, he may have a considerable propolis content. Propolis, which grows very hard and rigid at freezing temperatures, will also melt at a lower temperature than wax, and will fuse slightly if chunks of it are left in a pile at room temperatures. When it does, it is sticky. Then, mixed in quantity with wax, it makes the wax sticky. A cake of wax at room temperature should not be sticky, but with 3 or 4 percent of propolis in it, it will be.

Not only is propolis-contaminated wax dark in color, but it is unfit for the making of foundation because it stretches. Candles made from it leave a char which clogs the wick. So the dealer tests the beekeeper's wax when it comes in, and if it contains much propolis, he will pay less for it.

The beekeeper is likely to scream that he can't help it if his bees coat some of the wax, and the cappings. Actually, cappings that had been coated were tested, and they contained less than one percent propolis, which is not an objectionable amount.

How come, then, that the apiary owner's wax contained 3 or 4 percent? Because when he cut wax from the frames and scraped them, he put all these scrapings in his wax vat. He scraped off the propolis with the wax burr combs and tossed that in, too. And even on new frames which have only been used once, there's a lot of propolis.

So mostly the beekeeper is to blame for his own trouble. He either didn't take care, or his cupidity got the better of him and he threw in the propolis to add bulk and weight.

Beeswax usually sells for between four and five times the amount per pound that liquid honey will bring. There will be up to 40 pounds of cappings from a ton of honey, which is like a bonus check for up toward 200 pounds of honey to the beekeeper on each ton. His scrap wax will add to this take.

Beeswax that goes into candles or cosmetics is consumed.

But beeswax which is made into foundation goes on and on being useful to the bee industry, and may theoretically show up in the wax vat many times during its lifetime.

In the matter of equipment, I've told you earlier about three items that have been standard since the dim beginnings of the bee industry in the United States. These are the hive tool, the bee veil, and the smoker. No beekeeper would think of operating without them, and they have remained remarkably unchanged down through all these decades.

The hive tool I didn't describe. It is a flat metal blade with a fairly wide, sharpened edge for inserting between supers glued down with propolis. That edge can, in addition to prying, be used for whittling away burrs of comb, cutting out sections of comb, and for many other purposes. The other end is like it, but with the blade hooked over for scraping off propolis from comb honey sections, or from frames, or from the edges of supers.

Unless, after removing a frame or a super or a hive cover, the beekeeper gets it back exactly as it was, which is pretty unlikely, the uneven breaking away of the propolis will not allow it to fit down smoothly. Therefore anything with propolis on it must be scraped before it is returned to position. The hive tool was invented because of propolis. Without bee glue the need for such a tool would nearly disappear. There would be nothing to pry loose, nothing to scrape.

In southern states where bees have access to trees and buds with more adhesive gums in greater quantity than the ones available in the north, the problem is extreme. Boards are split in trying to pry supers loose. Frames are ruined in the same way.

It is so bad down there that just prying loose and scraping aren't always enough. The bees have been just too efficient with their glue.

So the beekeepers match the ingenuity of the bees. Many of them coat with grease any edges of supers or frames or covers that come together. They put it on the ends of frames, on the bottom board where the hive will rest, and most important of all, on the cover where it will set down on the top super.

The bees cement everything with propolis just as they did before. But propolis stuck to grease isn't really stuck at all. Removing cemented-down covers and supers with grease between them is more like taking candy away from a baby than like taking honey away from propolis-spreading bees.

In the South, beekeeping is a year-round proposition. There is no packing or moving inside to prepare the colonies to face winter. In some locations the bees may not make enough honey during several winter months to keep themselves. But they can fly out at all times and drop their feces. Brood rearing will start far, far earlier than it would up North. That is the basis of the package bee industry.

What is the beekeeper's routine? In the spring up North, he goes to his colonies and examines them to see how they wintered. He will use smoke at the entrance, and when he removes the cover. If his work was done well the fall before in preparing for winter, he should find his colonies in good condition. If those colonies were carefully packed, in a two-story hive with plenty of natural food, a young queen, plenty of pollen, the beekeeper should find little spring dwindling, dysentery and other ills that colony flesh is heir to.

The beekeeper's practiced eye must tell him from the things he sees when he opens each hive, what if anything he must do. He notes the brood chamber, the numbers of dead bees, the liveliness and general condition of the living, the condition of the queen, if he can see her (and if he can't no great harm is done because her condition is all too apparent in the brood chamber) the amount of pollen stores remaining for brood rearing, signs of mouse and skunk activity in the yard, and many other things. If the colonies were tar-paper packed, this must be removed as early as it is safe to do so.

The decisions he must make are important. Can he just put the cover back on, or must he feed this colony? Should it be honey, sugar water, pollen, or a combination of the three? Should he note down in his book that this colony needs requeening? Or have the queen cells in the brood chamber told him that the colony is about to either swarm or supersede and requeen itself? If it looks like swarming, he must decide what action he's going to take. Shall he destroy the cells, put on more room? Should that extra strong colony be divided to prevent swarming and provide a new colony? What is best for the colony and for its summer production of honey?

If the colony seems weak and has wintered poorly, should he provide a three-pound package of bees without queen from the South, or should be combine that colony with another weak one? Should he perhaps close the entrance even more on a weak colony? On a strong one, when the dandelion and orchard honey is coming in, should the entrance be opened wider than it is?

Ordinarily a super should not be added until the area below is almost full. But if this is an outyard and the beekeeper knows he cannot return for a considerable length of time, he may decide to add a super now to hold down the swarming instinct in his colony, and to make sure he doesn't lose valuable honey before his next trip because the bees have no place to store it.

Before he leaves the yard the beekeeper may spread poison food for skunks.

The super which the beekeeper put on may be filled with drawn-out combs from the year before. Or it may have only foundation.

Sometime, as near the main honeyflow start as possible, beekeepers may put a queen excluder between the first and second sections of the two-story hive. This confines the queen to the lower story from then on, and cuts her egg laying to about the amount needed to replace dying bees. The brood she has already laid in the upper story (or stories) in building up the colony to maximum strength, will continue to be serviced by the workers, who can pass easily between the wires of the excluder which are so spaced that the larger queen can't get through. The brood will hatch out, grow, and the cells will be cleaned and made ready. And if no more brood can be started above the bottom story, those cells will be filled with honey.

There will be a few swarms during swarming season that the beekeeper will want to save. Swarms from his hives in the outyards will, in all probability, be lost to him except as he is lucky, or is told that a swarm is hanging near one of his yards. Even then he may not have time to go after it.

He would, himself, be too busy to keep watch. Besides, he doesn't expect his colonies to swarm. He's either divided them artificially or removed queen cells, or just added so much space above them that he thinks the swarming has been taken care of in his outyard colonies.

Mainly though, once the honeyflow starts, the beekeeper will be engrossed in servicing his bees with enough supers. If he has plenty of extra supers ready, this presents only half the problem it presents when he runs short. In the latter case, to avoid loss of possible revenue, he must take the filled supers off, extract them, and put them back on again. No super should be extracted until it is ¾ capped in a dry area, and completely capped in a damp area. All this takes time.

In the outyards, as we have seen, it is sometimes necessary to add supers before they are actually needed. This should be avoided as much as possible. But it is better to give the bees too much space than too little.

When the bees cluster heavily on the face of a hive in ordinary weather and in a honeyflow, it usually means they are crowded for space. If the weather is very hot it may mean they are crowded, or it may mean they haven't enough opening for proper ventilation. In either event the beekeeper must act.

When the honeyflow is over, the beekeeper removes the supers. To do this he must first get the bees out of them. We have seen that he does this with a bee escape under the bottom super he is to remove, or with a carbolic acid pad placed under the hive cover. Commercial beekeepers use the pad because they can rid their supers of bees in a matter of minutes. They know just how to use it, how much acid to use, and how long to keep it on. Beginners should avoid it until someone has shown them the methods. In outyards the carbolic pad is especially helpful because without it two trips might be necessary for service, instead of just one.

If a beekeeper uses a bee escape, a Super Lifter is most helpful, too. With this ingenious gadget the operator can raise all the supers he intends to remove, swing them sideways, place the bee escape, and swing them back, all without danger of permanent harm to his sacroiliac.

In the fall comes the building up of colonies, requeening, manipulation of pollen and honey stores to ready the colony to make the best use of them in its winter cluster. Later still there comes the wrapping of the hives, and then the saying good-bye to them for the long winter.

But in the honey house, the work goes on. The frames of the supers that haven't been extracted must go through the machines. Their stores of honey must be handled, readied, packed, and shipped. This is the payoff. It must net the operator his winter's living, some extra, and enough to pay all bills till his checks for next year's honey start coming in. This long payless situation is alleviated in the South, for some, by roadside sales of honey throughout the tourist season. In the North there are roadside sales in late summer, from early-processed honey, and during the foliage season. After that any sales made at retail are likely to be made from the honey house. If a beekeeper has regular customers, he makes his deliveries.

The good beekeeper can weather a poor honey year with a better crop than the poor beekeeper. The good beekeeper may not be too badly hurt. But there will once in a great while be a season when there just isn't any honey made by anyone in a given area, good or poor at the business. In such calamity years the beekeeper can only live and operate on *his* surplus which he has carefully stored in square cells in a local bank. He must pay his help, buy his supplies, buy sugar if his bees didn't even make enough to winter. All he can do is hope for a bumper crop next year to make up. If he has regular customers, he may even buy honey wholesale from more fortunate areas, to pack and retail. This helps a little.

In between there is always the watch he must keep for the dreaded AFB and lesser diseases. There is the fight against enemies. There is the effort to convince agriculturists that they should spray orchards and other areas when there will be the least bee damage, both for their own good and for his. There will be the encounters with irate citizens who are positive that his bees menace the life and health of everyone around them. It's even hard to convince someone who has been stung by a wasp a quarter of a mile from a beeyard that the beekeeper shouldn't be outlawed by the legislature from the entire area.

He may, if he's big enough, want to experiment with new ideas and new gadgets. The University of Arizona recently announced a new device which, instead of uncapping, perforates the caps. The extractor removes the honey in the regular way, and the bees refill and are saved the time and material needed for another capping. But the machine must rough the cap because if it is left smooth the bees will just come along and repair it on the empty cell.

Or the beekeeper may want to experiment with various strains of the hybrid bees that are being developed. The *Wall Street Journal* said recently that the government was releasing some of the hybrids for private tests. In the tests performed by the developers, the hybrids had averaged over 200 pounds of honey per colony against a commercial national average of 54. Any beekeeper would be interested in such results if they should prove out in apiary tests, and if the hybrids could somehow be made available to him at a cost which wasn't prohibitive.

Charles Mraz, for one, is experimenting with the milking of venom from the bees by getting them, by electric shock, to sting a pad. He did some of this work in the South last winter. He takes the venom away in quantity, and he sells it to laboratories.

Many beemen work in their apiaries without bee veils. Many use veils but leave their hands bare so that they will be stung there and will know that the time has come to use more smoke. A. I. Root suggests a white coverall suit with hat and face screen attached, all in one piece. He suggests gloves.

In spite of the stings and the hard work and the occasional poor years, there are compensations and satisfactions. The beekeeper is his own boss. Usually he can, if he needs to, take what time off he needs. The northern operator can combine business and a Florida or California vacation, either with his own bees or working for someone else. In the North, if he chooses to stay there, his work is leisurely. It definitely is not under pressure in most cases. He has only so much work to do before he goes to the bees in the spring, and he can divide it into the available days in any way he sees fit.

There is a fine satisfaction in looking around at the honey house with its machinery and equipment. In the summer there is extreme satisfaction during honeyflow time in hearing the contented hum of his hives, seeing the clouds around each door, the businesslike attitude of the yard. All those thousands upon thousands of little insects are working intently making money for him.

The outdoor work is healthful work, the sounds and smells of the outdoors and particularly of the beeyard are to some people intoxicating. The beekeeper is very close indeed to nature. And whether because of the outdoor work, or because of the stings he receives, or for some other undetermined reason, beekeepers as a class have year after year been surprisingly free of the dreaded cripplers, arthritis and rheumatism. We'll speak more about that later. If the beekeeper is a boastful type, he can tell people he owns "five hundred buildings" or whatever the number. He's likely to make quite an impression until his hearers discover the size.

Beekeeping fits nicely with many other occupations—orchardist, market gardener, and many others. It even fits nicely with retirement.

So, despite drawbacks, the beekeeper is likely to be fiercely partial to his way of life, and to feel that he wouldn't swap places for any amount of money with the ulcer-bothered head of a big corporation, or the young man fighting his way up the ladder in a highly competitive city business world.

13

BEE HUNTING

There is, believe it or not, a sport called "bee hunting." And before you have visons of a redclad hunter carrying a shotgun or rifle, preceded by a hunting dog, stalking over the countryside trying to shoot a little half-inch long bee in flight, I hasten to disillusion you. You use a special little box that fits in your hand instead of a gun. And you aren't trying to shoot down one bee to get one drop of nectar; you're trying for the whole mass of boodle; the jackpot.

Like any other type of hunting, it is extremely rough on the hunted who happen to be unfortunate enough to be found. But it is not as rough on the victim as ordinary hunting is. It provides, like regular hunting, food for the hunter's table. It provides, too, exercise and excitement for him, and sometimes even a continuing income, which is more than can be said for success in ordinary hunting.

It has other advantages that regular hunting does not have. There is no chance of being accidentally shot and killed, a very real risk which the deer hunter runs. You may be stung, which provides the element of danger, but unless you're allergic to bee stings in the real sense and not in the slang sense, there's not much chance of death. Grade-school children can go bee hunting alone or with parents, and the ones I've introduced to the sport have had the time of their lives and loved it.

Too, it's fantastically inexpensive compared with any other sort of hunting; no guns, no shells, no fancy boots and expensive special clothing. Just that box, which you can make yourself, and a gob of honey.

The box which I always used was about 6 inches long, 3 inches wide, and 2½ inches high. But any old box would actually do. A special box, however, works a little better though not a lot better.

If the box has a sliding cover, that makes the capturing of a bee that much easier. If a tiny rectangle of glass is set into that sliding cover, and in turn has its own sliding cover, this allows you to see easier what your bee inside is up to.

You pick a country location which you know fairly well, and which is as far as possible from any apiary. The further you are from civilization, the harder it will be to find bees. But when you do find them, there will be much less chance that they belong in some beekeeper's hives.

Finding a bee that doesn't belong in an apiary is your primary aim. Near the spot on Lake Champlain where I spent my summers as a boy, there was a small wooded mountain which rose in farm land to about 1,200 feet. If you hunted the fields around that mountain and found a bee which headed directly toward the woods, excitement would rise in you, because you knew then that your expedition might be successful. The mountain was wide enough so that the bee couldn't possibly be heading for an apiary on the far side.

The whole sport is based on the fact that bees fly directly from the source of nectar to their homes. This is the "beeline" that you've heard spoken of so often.

You spot a bee on a flower. You open the sliding cover on the box. You hold the box on the palm of the right hand (or left if you're left-handed) in such a position that your first finger of that same hand can rest against the sticking-out edge of the partially open cover.

You hold the box's opening under the bee. With your other hand you slap (as gently as possible and still get the job done) the bee down into the opening, and instantly, with that first finger of the box hand, slide the cover closed. Now you've got a bee. You've got a very mad bee, as you can tell by the angry buzzing from inside the box.

Inside that box, at the end farthest from the opening (so that the bee when you slap her won't get her wings daubed) you have placed a tiny dish containing honey. Here again, you can put the honey on a piece of waxed paper if you don't have a tiny receptacle of some sort. But the little dish—we used one of those early-settler salt containers which are now so prized as antiques—will keep the honey from messing up the inside of the box, and thus daubing your bees as they buzz around in their first anger.

You carry the box to some sort of clearing where you can see well. And you find a resting place for it. A stump is good. Or, if it is farm land, a fence post. Get it up away from the ground, because you want to see your bee against the sky when she comes out.

Listen, then, with your ear close to the box, because the buzzing may have stopped. The bee is angry, and probably frightened at being confined. But she has this tremendous, urging instinct to take honey back to the hive. After she has calmed down a little that instinct will transcend even her anger and fear.

She'll find the supply of honey—not nectar but honey already cured and ready to store—and she'll postpone trying

to find a way out of this hateful prison until she can fill up
with that delightful food. Most trapped creatures wouldn't
react that way. Often animals, imprisoned, won't touch the
finest food. But they don't have that overpowering urge to
store for the common good which dominates the world of
honeybees.

So, if the buzzing has stopped you slide back the little
cover over the rectangle of glass in the main cover. If the
underside of the bee appears there at once, called by the light
and crawling upside down on the inside of the glass, you
slide the cover back over the glass and wait a while longer.

After a few minutes, try again. You can see now why the
glass is so helpful. Without it you'd have to open your box
to find out whether your bee was filling with honey or not,
and in doing so you'd run a heavy risk of losing your bee.
If you have to use a box with no glass in the cover, your only
course is to wait so long that you're positive the bee has
begun to fill herself. Even then you may find you guessed
wrong.

This time no bee appears at the glass. So, very cautiously
you slide the main cover open a crack. The opening should
be just large enough to allow the bee to come out easily.

Once you've done this, go lie down on the ground on your
stomach some twenty feet away from the bee box. And keep
your eyes glued on that opening. Sometimes in the middle of
filling herself the bee will see the opening, come out momentarily. But in almost every case she'll go back in again
and finish filling her honey stomach. If there are two or
more of you hunting, get yourselves spaced as evenly on the
perimeter of the circle surrounding the bee box as you can.

Finally, filled and heavy, the bee will come out. That's
when excitement will really make your heart pound. Because
now you'll find out whether you're going on with this, or

whether you've caught one of the millions of servants of some beekeeper.

The bee comes out and examines the box, the post and the area. You'll read that she'll circle to locate the place in her mind, exactly, and to orient herself for the trip home. Actually it's more a series of half circles, figure eights, and the like. She doesn't make ever-widening circles. She turns back, goes in the other direction. But the pattern keeps growing wider, and seems to be taking one direction more than any other. Finally she starts out in that direction.

Again, its not the "beeline" you read about and envision as being straight. It's a weaving line, but from the weaving you get the straight direction. She grows smaller and smaller in the distance.

And then, if you can still see her, she'll turn and come back part way, and start again in the direction she first took.

Now comes your knowledge of the terrain, especially of the apiaries in the neighborhood. Because if that beeline heads in the direction of an apiary, you must pick up your bee box and start all over again with another bee.

If, however, it goes in a direction that will lead to no apiary you know about, your elation can be unbounded. And you can leave your bee box right where it is. Because your bee will go to the hive, perform her little wagging dance, and pretty soon other bees will appear at the box. Your first bee, too, if you have any way of telling her from the new-comers, will return.

There'll be a wait, of course, its length determined by the distance of your position from the colony. But the waiting time can be well employed. You use it in making a rough map of the area. When the map is as accurate as you can make it, mark your present position, and mark on it too the beeline you have just established.

By that time, unless you're a faster worker than I am, a bee will have come from the colony and will have entered your open box on the fence post. Again establish the line, refine it if that is necessary, because as the bees get to know the location better, they'll pop out of the box and head for home with less and less half-circling. If you own a second bee box, your companion can take the other one and establish a new line some distance away with a new bee, while you're making your map.

Once you have the beeline established perfectly, and you have several bees flying to and from your bee box, you're ready for the next move.

When you have bees inside the box—several is best, but one will do—close the sliding cover, take the box and run, don't walk, in a direction roughly at right angles to the beeline you have established. But run carefully so as not to jar the box and its inmates any more than is absolutely necessary. Run as far as you can until you think that the bees inside will have had a chance to fill themselves and will begin to buzz around and possibly get daubed in trying to find a way out. In the meantime, leave a second box, or just a plain chunk of honey if you have only one box, on the original fence post so that other bees, returning, will maintain your original line for you while you're away with a few of their fellows.

When you have gone as far as you think the bees will stand, or as far as your too-much-food, too-many-cigarettes lack of condition will allow, you find another fence post for your bee box. Then you slide back the cover, throw your tortured, heaving chest onto the ground nearby, and watch the opening again. You have to be fast, because the bee or bees will boil out angrily. They've been cooped up when they wanted to carry honey home.

But that instinct to carry home and store will get the better of them again; they'll return and mark the place, half-circle, and figure-eight, and establish you another line.

Once it's established, put it onto your map just the way you did your first one. Then, where the two lines meet (if your calculations have been accurate) will be your bee tree. All that's left is to find it. But that's a lot.

That's the general principle of the thing. There are all sorts of refinements, many different types of bee boxes. And there are as many different methods, all within this general setup, as there are bee hunters.

After you have established the second line, some hunters established a third, even a fourth, in the same manner. Other hunters, after establishing two, carry their closed box with bees in it to the spot where the two lines meet. There they release the bees and establish their third lines, often within a hundred yards of the bee tree. Such a line, moved around a bit, helps a great deal in locating the bee tree if it is in dense woods and hard to find.

For the actual finding of the tree, there is no substitute for hard looking and probably a stiff neck. You walk systematically among the trees where you know the colony must be living, maneuver until you get every nub, every hole in every trunk and every branch against a patch of sky. In this way, and in this way only, can you be sure you'll see bees coming and going from their home when you finally find it.

Once you spot it, you can't mistake it. If it's a strong enough colony to merit your interest, there will be a dozen or more bees in the air outside waiting their turn at the entrance on any good day. There's no alighting board on a bee tree, and they either have to hover or light on the trunk near the opening. Furthermore, the wood at the rim of the hole is likely to look smooth and "used" because of the passing across it of so many thousands of bees so many times.

You're excited because you've won. You've found the bee tree you were after. Unlike other types of hunting, though, your reward is not immediate. You can "take up" the bee tree soon if you want to. But a course we consider more sensible, the one I have usually followed, is to wait and see whether or not the colony is able to winter. Because if they aren't able to winter, an oversimplification is that there wouldn't have been enough honey in there to make the effort of cutting the tree worth your while. Sometimes this rule wouldn't hold, of course. The colony could winter-kill from disease, cold or from any of a number of other troubles, even if they had a whopping excess of honey stored. But the rule is good enough, often enough, so that I usually stick to it.

If you're going to wait, you carve your initials on the tree trunk. This establishes your prior claim to the tree, and bee hunters, who are a pretty nice bunch of people on the whole, will mostly honor your claim. It's best, though, to carve the initials on the side of the tree where they'll be the least noticeable to a passerby. Because while bee hunters will usually honor your claim, some other hunters, either through ignorance or dishonesty, won't. And if the initials are prominent, they just call attention to that particular tree.

According to common law, the initials on the tree give you the ownership of the swarm and the honey, but not the right to cut the tree. Some states allow you to cut the tree if you pay the owner the value of it. This is not as great as it might seem. Since if a colony is living in a tree, that means per se that the tree is hollow and worth little except as firewood.

Usually the most practical way to handle the matter with a tree owner is to tell him you've found a bee tree on his property and want to take it up (cut it) for the honey. Tell him you'll give him part of the honey you get, and that you'll saw and pile the wood for him to use, and you'll have no problem. You don't have to tell him where the tree is until you see how the conversation is going.

We'll suppose now that your bee tree wintered and the colony went through the next honeyflow. You want to take it up and you have the permission of the landowner. What do you do?

You get a smoker, a bee veil, and some help. You'll need a chain saw (a crosscut saw if no chain saw is available), ax, wedges and sledgehammer, and some large pails or other containers for the honey. If you want to save the swarm, you'll need a vacant double hive with a few frames all drawn out and ready for storage and brood.

You cut the tree. Try to fell it in such a way that the opening will land facing up so that you can reach it easily with the smoke. Just before the tree is ready to go, you and your companions should don your bee veils, put on the gloves, tie your pants legs, and in other ways make yourselves ready to withstand the anger of the swarm. You get your smoker going nicely, and one of the party stands with it, ready to jump for the opening the moment the tree lands.

The tree crashes to earth with a mighty shattering of limbs. All other things being equal, it's best to land the tree on the side which has the most branches, to cushion its fall so that the honey and combs inside will be damaged as little as possible.

Instantly your smoker man jumps for the opening, blows smoke into it. Then he lays about him on all sides with puffs of smoke. Your saw man gauges the opening and the trunk, and figures how far the hollow extends above and below the hole. He (or they, if it's a crosscut saw) begins to saw through the log below where he thinks the honey storage may end. But he watches his saw, and if honey comes out on the teeth of it, he immediately pulls it out, moves down, and starts another cut farther from the opening. He may have to do this twice before he gets below the stored honey. If he does, you've got a bonanza.

After he has finally sawed through the log below the hole, he moves above and repeats the process there. All the while the smoker man is protecting him with smoke, every few moments turning back to the opening and giving that a few puffs.

Meantime, any other helper you may have can rap a few times on the trunk with ax or sledge. The bees seem dazed by the crash. Such blows on the trunk, together with the smoke, make them more docile as they fill their honey stomachs to be ready to move to a new location and start again, after the disaster that has befallen them.

When the center log each side of the hole has been cut free from the rest of the tree, you drive in the wedges with the sledgehammer on top of the log and split it lengthwise. When this work is done, the two halves of the log open up, and leave exposed the stores of the colony.

If you plan to save the swarm, look for the queen. If you can find her, clip the end of one wing and place her gently on a branch up from the ground close to the hive you have provided. The bees may find her there and begin to cluster around her. And by that time the air will be full of bees. Up where the opening used to be, bees returning from the field and finding nothing there, are circling, trying to decide what to do. If you can start a noticeable ball of bees around your queen, other bees will be called to it, will join it. Often, though, you can't get the queen, or the bees, to cooperate.

Often, too, you can't find her, especially if things are pretty badly broken up from the crash in the brood and storage chamber.

The comb will be in long strips, varying in shape and size with the inside shape of the hollow. They're reinforced, attached and placed with the ingenuity and ability of a graduate engineer.

The best honey will be in the far reaches. The brood and bee bread, will be nearest the opening. If there is a lot of honey, and if the combs were not too badly mashed in dropping the tree, you can cut up great chunks of honey-filled comb and fill your pails and other containers very rapidly.

The brood areas will likely overlap the honey areas. You can cut out whole chunks of pure brood and place them in your empty super above the hive you've provided. You're going to get some brood and a lot of bee bread in with your honey though, under the very best of conditions.

And the best of conditions are seldom allowed you. Things can get pretty crushed and mixed up in there, and at the worst you've got brood, bee bread, slivers of wood, wax, dead bees, sawdust, and even dirt which dropped from the upper reaches of the hollow, all mixed together in such a mess that you practically have to spoon it out. In this case, the chances of finding the queen or saving any of the brood are just about nil.

You load your containers of honey into your station wagon and head for home. If you've got a bit of a mess to contend with, all during the trip bees are likely to be hatching out of the brood and buzzing against the windows. Under these circumstances the honey will have to be strained through cloth. It must be allowed to drip a long while and must be thoroughly crushed to make sure no whole capped cells remain. Seldom have I seen pieces of comb in good enough condition so that they could be uncapped and run through an extractor instead of being strained.

The honey tastes strong. Everything that was crushed up into the mass from which you strained it, affects the taste. It tastes no more like extracted honey from a fine apiary, than campfire-cooked food tastes like the product of a gourmet kitchen. But I like it, and enjoy eating it, just the way a campfire meal on occasion is delicious. You wouldn't want a campfire meal every day, always. You wouldn't want wild honey always, either.

As for amount, I've seen three or four hundred pounds taken from a huge bee tree. I've also seen the time when you were hard put to it to salvage a couple of half pints of pretty wild-tasting fluid. It might have been stretching a point even to call it honey. You can never tell for sure how much there will be when the tree is big. When it's a small tree, you can be pretty sure the bees didn't have room enough to store very much worthwhile honey, and I for one wouldn't bother to take up the tree.

You go back when matters have quieted down at the tree, and try to hive your colony. If you found the queen, if the bees clustered around her, you may hive them easily. If matters didn't go well, the queen may have been lost, and in that case the bees remaining may finally go and try to join some other colony, singly. Sometimes they'll be accepted, especially in the peak of the honeyflow. Sometimes they'll be set upon by guards as robber bees and killed.

Occasionally the bees will cluster and swarm even though *you* missed the queen and thought she had been killed. They found her without you. This is a bonus. If you succeed in hiving the swarm, you leave them where they are for a few days to get established and start work. Then some night you come and move them to your apiary. Later you'll have to remove and replace the super where you set in chunks of brood. But the brood you did save should have helped them get re-established. For some time to come, you may have a continuing income from a fine colony of bees. You'll have to feed them that first winter, since you have stolen their stores. But this is a small price to pay for a strong healthy swarm. How you come out in saving the colony will, in the last analysis and barring accident, depend on how adroitly you handle the situation. Because the bees want to go on living as a colony, and re-establish themselves if you can give them enough help.

There are other ways you can insure yourself of the colony *before* you cut the tree. A. I. Root advocates the building of a platform high up in front of the entrance, big enough to hold a hive. On this platform he places his new hive with frames, and a new queen with a few attendant bees.

Then he installs a bee escape in the entrance to the hollow tree. This allows the bees to come out of the tree, but not go back in again. They'll come back from the field, find they can't get into their home, and finally enter the hive instead. Bees coming out will buzz around in bewilderment too. They too will finally join. The colony on the platform, finding a laying queen, room and brood, will begin to work. You can even set up a funnel running from the bee escape into one corner of the hive entrance. In this way the tree bees have to pass into the hive to reach the outside world, and this helps make them accept it when they return.

When they are well established, the hive is removed to the apiary, the tree is felled and the honey taken with a loss only of the few bees that have recently hatched out, and the old queen.

And I was told recently of a new plan made possible by the

invention of the chain saw. I did not see this personally, but this man tells me he cut a chunk out of the side of a bee tree while it was still standing. He did this by using the end of the chain saw. He removed this panel, robbed the colony of a reasonable amount of good honey, and then put back the chunk of the side of the tree, wiring it in place.

The bees sealed it with propolis, and went on living and working there with no more dislocation than they would have experienced if a super was removed. They wintered, and he took out his panel again the next year, with the same result. He swears he has a fine thing going for him there. I personally plan to try it the next time I'm ready to take up a bee tree, which through pressure of other affairs doesn't happen as often as I wish it did or as it used to. In the old days before the chain saw you couldn't have sawed out a panel without messing up everything inside the tree.

The first bee tree I ever found alone, I found when I was still under school age. My father had left me with the bee box at a big patch of buckwheat in bloom, simply loaded with bees. I established a line directly toward nearby Lake Champlain and directly away from any apiary. But I was too inexperienced to go on with it, and too impatient to wait for my father's return. I lay down on my back and looked up at the blue sky. At first I could see nothing. But when my eyes became accustomed to the blue and the rapid movement, I saw many bees from that buckwheat patch flying over me toward the lake. I got up and moved a hundred yards along the line, lay down and still saw bees flying. I did this over and over. But when I reached the woods I could no longer see the bees for the tree branches, and I went back for my father.

His whole attitude was, "There, there, of course you found a beeline."

But when I showed him, the condescending attitude of a grown-up for a child changed completely and he became as excited as I was. We began to scan trees, and I was the one who finally found the colony high in a tree on the very bank of the lake. I wouldn't hear of waiting a year, and when we took up the tree we got only four quarts of honey. But this I carried home to Worcester, Massachusetts, with me at the end of the summer, personally, in my suitcase (the four quart jars filled it) while somebody else had to carry my clothes in another suitcase.

So try bee hunting by all means. And I hope you enjoy it as much as I have. Find your tree, take it up. But get permission from the owner first. The one time I failed to do this, we had been told that the owner never granted permission, and we decided we were going to take the tree up regardless. I was in college at the time, and college boys have a tendency to be headstrong.

We waited until the owner was to be away for the day, then three of us drove down there. I was sitting in the back seat with a crosscut saw in my arms when we met the owner in his car. He had been late in getting started on his day away.

We cut the tree anyhow, and a few days later one of the other boys met the owner who said, "You and that Hoyt who likes bees were the ones who cut a bee tree on my land. I saw the three of you driving down that way."

My friend said in a shocked and innocent voice, "Why no; you're wrong. You've just proved it. Hoyt and that other guy are city bred. You know yourself that they wouldn't understand how to use a crosscut saw, or cut a tree. City boys don't know those things. Besides, they would be too soft to do the work even if they did know. You understand that."

And the man said, "Yes, I guess you're right. I hadn't

thought about it just that way." And he went away convinced.

So get permission. The friend who helps you might not be as convincing a liar as mine was. And even if he should be, it's disconcerting to find that the world can be so easily convinced of your ineptitude and lack of stamina.

I4

BEE VENOM

When a honeybee stings you, the venom that her torn-out
poison sac injects into you through the stinger is a waterlike
liquid. It has a strong odor which some scientists have
likened to the smell of ripe bananas. At least one scientist
with a dedicated approach to the matter must have tasted it,
because the books say it has a bitter taste. This item of information is strictly secondhand as far as I'm concerned. This
tasting wasn't, actually, as foolhardy as it might seem, because stomach fluids destroy bee venom quickly; taken in-
ternally it has little or no effect. Neither does it have any
effect on unbroken skin.

The chances are you won't be very interested in all this at
the moment. It's going to hurt like crazy (unless you're a beekeeper; most of them are pretty thoroughly immune and
feel nothing worse than a pinprick) and you are going to be
very busy being your own choreographer while you accom-
pany your dance vocally with the loud music of complaint.

You aren't going to be even mildly interested, for instance,
in the fact that F. Flury, a toxicologist of the University of
Wuertzburg, found that bee venom contains tryptophan,

choline, glycerin, phosphoric acid, palmitic acid, fatty acid which won't crystallize, a volatile acid which is probably butyric, and an unknown, nonnitrogenous substance. The last item he feels is the roughest on your system. The active agent is always in combination with lecithin. Strictly bee venom does *not* contain any formic acid.

You probably couldn't care less at the time about the fact that a number of substances will destroy it: among them, chlorine, bromine, and alcohol. You won't be particularly alarmed that the bee will die; you'll be vindictively delighted that she will. You'll alternate between being afraid you yourself are going to, and wishing you would. If you're not stoical by nature, you'll likely take it big.

A small round red swelling with a red spot in the middle will appear where you were stung. This is a called a "wheal." If the stinger and poison sac are still in the wound, you definitely must not squeeze the place, or grab the sac and pull it out. Either course will squeeze all the poison into your system. Further, you must not leave it in there because the stinger is split into two barbed shafts, and with each side being twitched alternately by attached muscles even after death while the barbs allow no backtracking, it works its way farther in and manages to pump all the poison into you if given time.

The correct procedure is to press a thumbnail on your flesh near the stinger. Then slide it against the stinger shaft, partly under the poison sac. Continue the sliding pressure and you will force the stinger up and out, and you will not have forced much poison through it.

Eventually the swelling will go down and the place will stop hurting. If you get mixed up with a whole lot of hornets or wasps you may have a lot of trouble just because of the amount of poison they manage to inject. Honeybees aren't anywhere near as likely to attack you in quantity as are hymenoptera that can sting again and again without harm to themselves. But sometimes they do attack in numbers. And if they do, you're in just as much trouble with them as with hornets or wasps.

This matter of stinging breeds on itself. Tests have shown that if a pad containing bee venom is inserted in a hive, the bees nearby, when they smell it, become very agitated and seem to be looking for the danger that such a smell indicates to them. They act as if they want to get into the battle. If bees outside a hive smell the pad, some of them will fly at and attack and sting anything that is moving. A beekeeper whose gloves, if he uses them, have been stung a lot of times, will find that such stingings begin to multiply rapidly. But if he puts on a clean pair of gloves, the colony will usually calm down at once.

Everyone understands that bees sting to protect their home. Yet if a beekeeper takes the home apart carefully, they may not sting at all. Charlie Mraz works among his colonies in summer bare to the waist. He's seldom stung. But if anyone bangs into a hive, or breaks it apart ruthlessly, he'll be stung.

The other reason is not so well known. Bees sting, too, when something goes wrong. If sudden rain cuts off a heavy honeyflow, they'll sting angrily. If you stand in front of the hive entrance when they are coming back loaded, and block them off, they'll sting you. If it's cold, miserable weather, they're not the same docile swarm that they were the day before, during good weather. If you open the hive when they can't go to the field, you'll get a very different reception from the one you'll get when nectar is coming in rapidly and the young bees are the only ones at home. If your bees are robbing out a weak colony and you remove the robbed hive before they finish, those bees will attack anything or anybody that moves. And probably try to start robbing every colony in the place, besides.

It can be seen, then, that with this behavior knowledge the ordinary person can easily avoid contact with honeybees, and especially with angry honeybees. But hornets and wasps are a different matter. You don't always see the paper nests till it's too late. You may rap your head against one. You may step on a hole in the ground that is being used by hornets as an entrance to their underground nest. You may start to remove a pile of rubbish next to the garage and find that you've disturbed a hornets' nest.

In such a case you're probably going to be stung. But you should hold it to a minimum by moving very quietly, just oozing away till you have put as many things between you and the angry householders as possible. And above all, don't flail at your attackers. That won't do the slightest good, and will call all the others.

It will be hard to do, but you should put both hands over your eyes and as much of your face as possible, giving yourself only a tiny crack between fingers for vision, while you are slipping away with a minimum of body movement.

Once while I was in grade school, a friend of mine and my father and I were picking raspberries and we disturbed a yellow jackets' nest. My father and I, in line with the advice my father called to us instantly, very quietly moved behind the nearest bushes, then a tree trunk, then more bushes, and came out very well. But my friend yelled, and stood and flailed, and then ran screaming and waving his arms. And he was stung terribly. He was sick and his face swelled until he couldn't see out of his eyes.

Many people are stung in their cars. They set the "no-draft" wing at an angle to scoop fresh air in against their faces. A bee, hornet or wasp hits this, is angled against the face and stings convulsively even though she is probably dying from the blow she has received. The car's resulting angling off the road and crash into a tree is spectacular and sometimes fatal. If you accept a little less air and angle the no-draft wing slightly away from you, you may live longer.

If a live bee enters your car and buzzes against the windows or a windshield, don't risk an accident by trying to swat her. Against glass she feels trapped, and is interested only in getting out, not in leaving the glass to attack you. You'll have plenty of time to pick a safe stopping place. Then you can steer the insect out an open window with a folded road map.

And don't think a dying insect can't sting. I cut a honeybee in half with the lawnmower a couple of years back and it was thrown against my bare shin. The resulting convulsive sting I got from the business end causes me to state without fear of successful contradiction that a sting from half a honeybee is just as painful as from a whole one. A wasp once crawled under my wife's pillow while we were sleeping on the porch of our cottage in the fall. She reached under for a handkerchief in the night, and she still doesn't think that my startled reaction to the resulting thrashing was sympathetic. For years afterward she looked under the pillow at night.

Yellow jackets enjoy building a paper nest under the overhang of a country building. It's very small when they start it. But by the time you notice it, it is likely to have taken on the general contour of an oversized, old-fashioned football.

The best method of handling these is preventive. I own 28 buildings next to Lake Champlain, and each week I have a boy examine the overhangs for yellow-jacket nests. You can rid yourself of a small nest, with a pole, in broad daylight.

But if the nest gets ahead of you and grows large, you must wait till night. You must put on heavy gloves, climb a ladder carrying a burlap bag. You pinch the nest off with the mouth of the bag as if you were choking someone to death. Then you tie the mouth of the bag with the nest safely inside, pour turpentine on it away somewhere, and touch a match to it. If the nest is built into a corner and you can't pinch it off, make a torch of turpentine-soaked rags on the end of a sharpened stick. Stick this in the ground eight or ten feet from the nest at night. Light the torch and knock down the nest with a stick and get away fast. The yellow jackets, seeing the flickering moving flame, will attack it and have their wings singed off and drop to the ground where they're reasonably harmless. Don't try to use a blow torch; I know of one man who burned his house down trying to burn out a yellow-jacket nest.

If bees take up residence between the outside and inside walls of your house (and if there is a small knothole or crack this makes an excellent setup from a honeybee's point of view, with wonderful storage between two or more studs) don't plug the hole, under any circumstances.

If you plug it in the daytime, all the field bees will return, find it plugged and their queen inside. They'll go almost berserk trying to get to and free her. And the whole area will be no safe place for man or beast as they swoop onto anything that moves. A man in Memphis did this a few years back and was literally a prisoner in his own home for days.

If you plug the hole at night you're not much better off, because 50,000 prisoners trying to find some way out, will sooner or later, before they die, find or chew their way through the inside wall, and nobody will be interested in living in *that* house for a while.

You can't get rid of them with household insect sprays, because the hole is too small. It's a job for a beeman or an exterminator. The beeman will hive the colony with a hive on a stepladder, using the process much as I described it in the chapter on bee hunting. He'll use a bee escape and queen excluder and a funnel and a new queen. Once he's finished and has all but a few of the bees, he'll plug the hole so the stores can't be robbed out or a new swarm take up residence.

If you insist on attacking the matter on a do-it-yourself basis, run a garden hose from the exhaust pipe of your car into the bee hole at night and plug around the hose so that it is airtight. Then let the motor run for a good long time. But be sure the house beyond is ventilated well, since carbon monoxide is deadly and odorless; if it should seep through cracks in the inside wall it might kill people.

One person out of every several thousand is allergic to bee venom. Such people don't react simply with that wheal I described. But almost at once he or she reacts with red skin blotches in parts of the body far removed from the stung area. In violent reactions the person will go into shock, be cold, clammy, incoherent, nauseated, have diarrhea. The blood pressure may go very low, the tongue swell, and the pulse become thready. He or she may go into a coma.

If you have ever been stung and had any part of such a reaction, you are literally like a person smoking atop a gasoline tank. You can, very possibly and very literally, die at any time you are stung again. I can't emphasize strongly enough that you should read what follows and take the precautionary steps recommended. Don't put it off! It may save your life!

Let me tell you of one or two incidents. We had a guest a

few summers ago at the resort which I own and operate on Lake Champlain. She was stung by a yellow jacket and had a very violent reaction.

Luckily Dr. J. F. Kilgus, who is director of health services for state employees of the state of Connecticut, a many times guest of ours, was in camp. We called him and he was there in moments.

He gave her, among other things, an epinephrine (adrenaline) injection. She responded quite rapidly. After she'd been taken to her cottage, one of the bewildered watchers said, "But Doc, just one little sting and all that. Could she really have died?"

Doctor Kilgus told us, "The sting from one bee can certainly do it. On one occasion a truck driver was carried to me unconscious. He had stopped his truck on a hill, got out and collapsed. A following truck driver rushed him to me. He had gasped out the word 'bee' as the other man reached him; otherwise he would probably have died, because we would not have found the sting mark in time and might have treated him for a heart attack. We wouldn't have dared use adrenaline. A girl up in Quebec named Dube was stung by a single bee and died within twenty minutes. A man in Caldwell, New Jersey, was stung once and died before a doctor could get there. Just this summer my own daughter, Bobbie Jean, became unconscious from a single sting."

If you are allergic to bee venom you have two things going for you. First, your sensitivity can be cured through treatment by a competent allergy expert. And second, you aren't going to die the first time you have a violent reaction.

The sensitivity has to be built up in your system, just like sensitivity to penicillin. You aren't going to die the first time you have a violent penicillin reaction. But if you do get one, then the next time you may die. Or the time after. A person sensitive to penicillin should wear a tag, so stating, around his neck so he won't be given a shot sometime while he's unconscious.

In the same way, bee venom sensitivity has to be built up. You won't die the first time you have a serious reaction, as I said, but the second or third time you might. The reaction will keep getting worse each time until one of them will definitely kill you.

The thing to do is start treatment. An allergy expert, with the use of patch tests on your skin, will determine your "threshold dosage"; how much you can stand. Then he will inject serum prepared from the venom of the insect in an amount below that dosage. He'll give you increasing doses at regular intervals until your immunity is complete. Once it's complete, you could stand stings easily that would have killed you before.

After you are once immunized you can live a completely normal life as regards hymenoptera. But you must return periodically once in so many months—whatever number your doctor prescribes—and get a booster shot to keep from gradually losing your immunity.

While immunity is being attained, carry with you on your person at all times antihistamine or Isuprel-Franol tablets. If you're stung, pop one under your tongue instantly and head for a doctor.

Dr. Kilgus has asked that Isuprel-Franol tablets be carried in highway maintenance crew trucks and police cars in Connecticut in case of stings. "Before we started that practice," he said, "stings were the largest single cause of lost time among the highway crews."

It's as easy as that. If you *ever* have a serious reaction to a sting, go get yourself immunized. Any other course is foolhardy.

This isn't even a terribly expensive process now, as it was when immunity experiments were first begun. Dr. Mary Loveless, of New York Hospital, Cornell Medical Center, has immunized patients with as few as six yellow-jacket venom sacs, the contents of which she injected in gradually increasing doses during a single sitting of from three to five hours. Other doctors have also achieved satisfactory results in the course of one long visit by the patient, but this hurry-up type of immunization is still considered highly controversial by many allergists.

One woman who had a daughter who was allergic to bee stings kept the girl indoors all summer instead of taking her to a doctor for immunity. A few shots would have let the child go out and play with her friends; as it was, she gazed at them out the window all summer.

Dr. Harold Medivetsky, allergy specialist of the University of Vermont Medical College, says that a venom-sensitized person is definitely warned that he has this condition by a lesser reaction before he has the fatal one. There have been cases where the relatives of a dead man said they never knew of his having had a serious reaction earlier. But Dr. Medivetsky thinks the man did not tell his family, because the sensitivity just has to be built up somehow. It can't be there lethally without having been built up. Certainly nobody was able to check with the victim.

Unfortunately there are people who, through ignorance or apathy, have a serious reaction to a sting and do nothing about it. They don't even carry antihistamine or Isuprel-Franol. This, in my opinion, is just asking for it.

A case in point is the woman I mentioned above who had the reaction at my camp. I became so interested in venom allergy because of the incident, that I looked up the available information and then talked with many medical experts on the subject.

I felt from what I learned that the one in thousands who has this condition should be warned. His life was just as dear to him and to his family as anyone else's life would be to *his* family. And the records showed that there was an overwhelming chance he wouldn't realize the increasing danger after he had been through his first systemic reaction. There was an even greater chance that unless somebody shocked him into action, he wouldn't do anything about it even if he did realize it. So I wrote an article on the subject for the *Saturday Evening Post* which I fondly hope, with their tremendous circulation, saved lives. The shocker element was that more people are killed in the United States by bee stings than by rattlesnake bites.

The woman read my article in the *Post.* Dr. Kilgus advised immunization shots for her. But those matters seem far away to us when we are perfectly well. She meant to do something about it. But she put it off.

The next summer, the afternoon she was to leave us after her vacation, she was dressed for travel and was saying goodbye to friends in the lawn chairs, among them Dr. Kilgus's wife and mine. She was stung by a yellow jacket.

My wife, knowing the situation, ran for the doctor. The woman got to her cottage close by, under her own power. Inside she suddenly collapsed. The doctor was there in moments.

And then began a very terrifying fight. The doctor used Isuprel-Franol, yet she went into a coma in spite of it. Her reaction the year before had been bad. This was infinitely worse.

He gave her an adrenalin shot and she roused momentarily

from her coma, and then lapsed into it again. He thought he had lost her, as there seemed to be no pulse. But he roused her again. And again she drifted away. Fighting with more adrenalin and in every other way he knew, he brought her back each time that she had apparently gone. The last time that she roused, he popped an Isuprel-Franol tablet under her tongue. A few moments later the waxy white suddenly left her face, color flowed in, and he was pretty sure he had won about as close a brush with death as he had ever waged successfully. She remained in bed the rest of that day and finally started home on the next day, still very weak.

There is absolutely no question but that she would have died had not Dr. Kilgus been seconds away. Her husband knew it and she knew it. That time she swore to him that she would get immunity.

When we got our Christmas card from her, she told us on it that she had finished her course of shots and was now safe. She will, as I have explained, return to her doctor once every year or less as he decides, for her booster shot. But she will never again have any fear, more than of the momentary pain and discomfort the rest of us get, of being stung.

On the other side of the coin, it is just as silly for a person who does not have a bee venom allergy—and there are thousands of normal-reaction people to every one of the others—to go into panic and call a doctor because he's stung. Remember, the fact you are sensitive to ragweed and other things, does not in any way, of itself, mean you're sensitive to bee venom. If you get the normal hurt, and wheal, and swelling from a sting, don't waste the doctor's time and yours. Put some mud on the place and try to act like the stoical hero your wife probably thinks you are. If you're stung by a whole lot of insects at once, though, best see your doctor. There could be trouble, not from an allergy angle, but from having that much poison in your system.

To sum up, then, bee venom allergy cases are few among us, but they are deadly. If you are so sensitized, then each reaction will be worse than the previous one till you die. But you can get immunity easily, with comparatively little expense. And if you don't, in the language of high society, you've got rocks in your head.

No discussion of bee venom is complete without mention of the controversy regarding bee venom as a cure for arthritis and rheumatism. You, the reader, should know there is such a controversy. And you should be given the arguments impartially that each side puts forth. When I get through I expect to get about the same number of letters from each side passionately accusing me of selling out to the opposition.

Both sides agree that the whole matter grew out of European folk medicine. By word of mouth, European peasants and, later, the farmers in this country, when medicine was in its infancy here and when barbers who doubled as doctors bled anybody for anything he had wrong with him, passed along the word that bee stings would cure arthritis and rheumatism.

This may have been because beekeepers with arthritis or rheumatism have always been scarcer than hen's teeth. Dr. Herman N. Bundesen said in his syndicated medical column of December 31, 1958, "About 11,000,000 Americans suffer from arthritis, rheumatism or one of the other rheumatic diseases. Chances are overwhelming that not a single one of them is a beekeeper!"

One side to the controversy claims there just aren't any beekeeper-arthritics. The other side says that if this is true it's because beekeeping is heavy work and a person who has these diseases couldn't carry it on. Pro Venom then gives cases where people who had arthritis started keeping bees (and being stung) and were cured. Con Venom says those people probably would have gotten over it anyway. Or only *thought* what they had was arthritis.

It's a touchy subject. I ran up against it after the *Post* article I mentioned above. In the article I said, "I know several people who have deliberately pressed bees against their flesh, in the hope that the resulting stings would help their rheumatism or arthritis. A majority of arthritis specialists have stated emphatically that bee stings do nothing for these maladies, and that such an action can be highly dangerous. Yet this practice has persisted through the centuries."

I thought I'd been pretty impartial. When the article came out a near neighbor took me to task for saying bee venom didn't help. It was in vain that I tried to explain to him that I had only been quoting the arthritis experts, giving both sides. He told me his own story in detail to try to prove that they were wrong.

He had developed considerable pain which had been diagnosed by a physician as arthritis. He had been treated in the usual manner and the pain had increased instead of decreasing. The treatment had done no good. His wife had suggested bee stings and he would have none of them. One day he came home and she was there with a friend who had some bees in a small box, and a pair of tweezers. She and the friend said they were going to let the bees sting the areas of my neighbor's pain.

He said the heck they were. But many a married man knows the end result of the argument. He finally let her hold the bees one at a time against his flesh with the tweezers.

They stung him and it hurt like fury. And he was mad

and disgusted and said so. He said he'd done it, and now they should be satisfied and, believe him, that was the end of *that*. He intended to punch the next person who held a bee against him, right in the nose.

He told me he was completely convinced it would do no good. He had submitted only to keep peace in his family; wives were hard to get and he was hungry and she was obviously going to keep arguing till he gave in.

The next morning he had no pain at all. And to this day he has had no recurrence. No pain whatever, after months of it. And he was pretty indignant about ". . . your saying it does no good."

I spoke about this to a doctor friend. He said, "Let's assume that he's not lying and that it happened just that way. What would have happened if he'd done that and he'd been allergic to bee venom?"

Well, of course the answer is that he would have been in critical condition, even might have been dead if he'd had any previous serious reactions. If it was his first reaction it would probably have scared his wife and his friend out of a year's growth.

"That's what we mean by saying it's extremely dangerous. Believe me the medical profession tested the ingredients of bee venom many years ago at the time a man inadvertently tangled with a beehive, was severely stung and had his arthritis disappear. Doctors experimented and there were no effects from their injections one way or the other. There's just nothing to it. And it's dangerous because of a possible allergy."

I went back to the other side with this statement. I was beginning to feel like the shuttle train between Grand Central and Times Square.

Pro Venom snorted considerably about medical experiments with bee venom. "Here," he said, "read these." And he gave me Dr. Bodog Beck's book *Bee Venom Therapy,* and a later one, *Bee Venom* by Dr. Joseph Boardman.

I read them. Both doctors readily admitted the tests made by medical scientists. But both said at the time it was generally and erroneously believed formic acid was the base of bee venom and was its active ingredient. After the dramatic cure of the man stung by bees, the testers had injected pure formic acid into arthritis patients and nothing had happened. All that proved, according to these Pro Venom doctors, both members of the American Medical Association, was that formic acid had no effect on arthritis. But it certainly didn't prove bee venom, which now · experts agree contains *no* formic acid, didn't affect arthritis. They claimed that to this day the controversy remains at this point, the medical scientists claiming exhaustive and negative tests, the venom people claiming that the tests were made with the wrong material and that they can't get medical periodicals which carry advertising to print the results of any later tests with actual bee venom.

I talked with another doctor about the matter. He said that if the tests were significant they'd be printed. He mentioned formic acid tests. He felt that pressing bees against flesh was like old tribal rites. And even its most ardent proponents didn't claim cures all the time.

The other side countered by saying they felt the same about live bees. All their work now was done with patch tests first to avoid any danger with an allergic patient, and hypodermic needle injections of a commercial bee venom product. And they certainly didn't claim (or get) cures in all cases. A typical test with 120 patients showed 65 cured, 24 materially helped and 31 not helped at all. But 15 of those

31 had Polyalgias (endocrine) which didn't respond much in testing 25 cases; only 4 cures and 6 helped. Subtracting those 15 would make the tests of the other 6 types of chronic Polyarthritis more impressive.

And Dr. Boardman says that cortisone and other hormone steroids commonly used in treatment of arthritis can't approach these results percentagewise, and if used over long periods produce side effects including "mental changes, edema, hypertension, heart failure, impaired wound healing, diabetes, peptic ulcers, moon face and buffalo hump." He claims that even in the cases where bee venom did no good, no *harm* would be done (if injected after a competent patch test) because there are no side effects whatever from bee venom in such doses.

Con Venom says that cortisone and kindred steroids admittedly have side effects, but in never more than 44 percent of cases and in some areas as low as one percent of those tested. "They're not good but they're the best we have. How is bee venom supposed to help?"

Doctors Boardman and Beck say that bee venom expands restricted blood vessels and through these brings the body's firemen rushing to the area to fight the fire. In doing so they also flush away and destroy the poisons that cause arthritis. They say it very scientifically and exactly; the above is my own oversimplification of their medical terms.

Con Venom is not convinced. "If there were any good in it, doctors would have found it out and used it long ago. They're a dedicated group with open minds on all cures satisfactorily proved."

Pro Venom says that the controversy has become so inflamed and the word "venom" is so wrong for a cure to start with, that the medical journals automatically refuse any writing about experiments with it. And the doctors, too busy to experiment on their own, therefore just don't ever gain access to the experiments and facts.

Boardman cites case after case. But to me these are impersonal "Patient A and Patient B" cases. And I find they don't impress me the way I was impressed by my near neighbor, whom I know personally.

And so the controversy rages, each side completely convinced it is right. On one side an array of doctors, only a few of them from this side of the Atlantic, swearing by the treatment. On the other side, the American Medical Association, just as convinced bee venom treatment is of no value. The 11,000,000 arthritis sufferers, meantime, wish and pray it might *be* a cure or help for some 72 percent of their numbers (nearly 8 million individual sufferers). But until it is generally accepted they intend to stick with their doctors.

So that is the story of that amazing, that incredible insect, the bee. She gives us lessons in selflessness and community enterprise. She fertilizes our crops; without her the vast multitudes of the world's people would starve or be forced to come up with some other means of pollination. She gives us millions of dollars' worth of food, sweet and predigested for easy assimilation by infants and invalids. Even the venom from her protective weapon, which can kill certain of us, is being tested in the hope that it may cure a great national crippler.

Our world would be a very different, rather drab place without the bee.

INDEX